ACCLAIM FOR WAKING MATHILDA A MEMOIR OF CHILDHOOD NARCOLEPSY

"This story envelopes us because of its profound vulnerabilities, its infuriating injustices, its dogged love, its honest faith. Claire Crisp draws us into their family story with intimate candor and tender courage. She does not overtalk the power of the events themselves. Instead, she manages to open windows into moments, feelings, relationships, systems, decisions, and questions that allow the reader to walk within an extraordinary medical and human journey. Her story has become her family's story. Their story becomes part of our stories, which in all our differences are also stories of raw vulnerability and strained hope."

—Mark Labberton, President of Fuller Theological Seminary

"One of my favorite sayings goes something like this: "If you try to tell a 'universal' story, you'll connect with no one in particular. But tell an infinitesimally particular story, and you've found a key that unlocks every human heart." Time and again, I find myself returning to Waking Mathilda, and not just because Claire Crisp knows how to create a compelling narrative. I return because her writing—in all its concrete particularity—gives voice to my own struggles both as a parent and as a chronic sufferer. Yes, these stories are about this woman and these children and this family's struggle to care for one another in and through a set of incredibly difficult circumstances. But that's exactly the point. Waking Mathilda is universal because, in them, we encounter something deeper and more profound: what it means to be a human."

—Kutter Callaway, PhD, assistant professor of theology and culture at Fuller Theological Seminary, and author of Watching TV Religiously

"As a parent of a child with multiple disabilities, the world can often be a frustrating and lonely place. I've found a source of comfort and solidarity in Claire Crisp's Waking Mathilda. Her writing is vulnerable, beautiful, and insightful. Though her daughter's needs are significantly different than my son's, and thus her family's challenges are different than my own, nevertheless I am reassured through Waking Mathilda that others stand in sympathetic solidarity."

—Kevin Timpe, PhD, William Henry Jellema Chair in Christian Philosophy at Calvin College

"Claire Crisp has just articulated the heart of a mother. Her remarkable story is not her own. It is the shared trial of keeping her girl alive and her family intact. Her daily, and nightly, grief, weariness, grit and truth light a path of hope for our own pain. Her ferocity is inherited by her daughter and in Waking Mathilda rubs off on each of us. Thank you for teaching us how to fight the good fight mighty in battle."

—Nada Jones, Founder of nadajones.com and Libertyforher.com

"Waking Mathilda is a beautifully written account of a family inflicted with narcolepsy. Narcolepsy while often invisible to the world so profoundly affects everything in one's life while it's ripples can't help but impact loved ones as well. Although Claire's memoir is the tragic story of one young child and one family, anyone who's life is touched by narcolepsy will identify with and enjoy Waking Mathilda."

—Mali Einen, PWN and former Clinical Research Coordinator at Stanford University, Current Manager of Patient Support Services and Patient Advocacy at Jazz Pharmaceuticals

"This book dives into a world of searching for answers to an undiagnosed medical disorder. The reader will gain a deeper understanding of narcolepsy and how it is a 24-hour medical disorder, expanding way beyond the idea that narcolepsy means people are a little extra sleepy. I have a child with narcolepsy and Claire's words stirred many buried emotions I experienced during my son's diagnosis period."

—Monica Gow, Co-Founder, Wake Up Narcolepsy

"This marvelous, moving book by Claire Crisp is a riveting chronicle of a loving parent's determined efforts to give her chronically ill child a chance and to keep the whole family afloat around the unrelenting needs imposed by her child's disability. It is not just a beautifully written story about a child's suffering matched by a mother's love. It is a story of faith that can light up the dark places of our lives. Nothing can make a child's suffering acceptable. Nothing can take away a parent's pain at being unable to make that suffering go away. But, with wit, with self-deprecating humor, with powerful and intelligent faith, Claire Crisp has written a book that illumines the strength of the human spirit and the depth of human love in suffering. It is a gem."

—Eleonore Stump, Robert J. Henle Professor of Philosophy, Saint Louis University, author of Wandering in Darkness: Narrative and the Problem of Suffering

WAKING MATHILDA

A Memoir of Childhood Narcolepsy

Palace Gate Press

Copyright © 2017 by Claire Crisp

Palace Gate Press

WAKING MATHILDA: A MEMOIR OF CHILDHOOD
NARCOLEPSY.

All rights reserved. Printed in the United States by Palace Gate Press.
No part of this book may be used or reproduced in any manner whatsoever
without written permission except in the case of brief quotations embodied
in critical articles and reviews. Originally published in ebook and
paperback.

Cover art & design by *Jonathan Green*
Author photography by *James Farlow*
Photo of Mathilda provided by Claire Crisp

www.claireccrisp.com

ISBN: 978-0-9986940-2-3
Book design by *James Farlow*

Printed in the United States of America
10   9   8   7   6   5   4   3   2   1

Names and minor details of medical professionals have been changed
to protect their identities.

For Oliver
and our children

Liberty Alice
Elliot Anselm
and
Mathilda Anais

Afoot and lighthearted, take to the open road,
Healthy, free, the world before you,
The long brown path before you, leading wherever
you choose.
Say only to one another:
Camerado, I give you my hand!
I give you my love, more precious than money,
I give you myself before preaching or law:
Will you give me yourself?
Will you come travel with me?
Shall we stick by each other as long as we live?

—from "Song of the Open Road" by Walt Whitman

Contents

Author's Note

"I soothe my conscience now with the thought that it is better for hard words to be on paper than that Mummy should carry them in her heart."

—Anne Frank

When the World Health Organization announced a global pandemic of the H1N1 virus in June 2009, it was anticipated that the new strain of Swine Flu would target the young and potentially claim as many people as the Spanish Influenza of 1918—millions. The British Government responded to this warning by supplying a vaccine, one that they claimed was both safe and effective, but one that had not been tested on children. General practitioners were financially incentivized to vaccinate as many of the population as possible. As with all parents of children under five, we received a letter strongly recommending the vaccine.

What emerged in 2010 was the realization that the new strain of H1N1 was not the threat predicted; no more lives were claimed than in any other flu season. Yet for the thousands of vaccinated children across Europe, 1500 already had begun to display bizarre neurological symptoms. For them it was too late. By the time each of those children had been diagnosed with narcolepsy, an incurable sleep disorder, the 70,000 neurons they needed to regulate sleep and wakefulness had been destroyed.

I have written this memoir as a mother who lost and regained a daughter; as a mother who, in the quest of waking Mathilda, has sought to illuminate the myths surrounding a condition that afflicts the mind by night and body by day—one that is under-diagnosed, under-recognized and under-reported. Mathilda's descent into narcolepsy, the hospital admissions and battle for treatment within the confines of socialized health care in England are memories so raw, it is as though they happened yesterday.

Yet six years into caring for a young child with narcolepsy, I am only too aware of the impact of my own sleep deprivation. Throughout this journey, I have turned to the pages and pages of her medical notes, letters between doctors and a journal I kept at the time: a small leather-bound notebook once used for scribbling ideas, magazine cuttings of pretty backyards and academic resources for our older two children. Those entries dried up and were replaced with hospital phone numbers, prayers and lists of new symptoms as they transpired over the months. Friends and family who observed Mathilda's decline in England offered helpful insights into both the baffling display of symptoms and the impact of her deterioration on all five members of my family. I have also relied on video footage and interviews with doctors who played a significant role during the time Mathilda remained undiagnosed.

What follows, then, is a recounting, to the best of my

abilities, of the last year and a half we lived in England. I have not, could not, in any way attempt to understand or rationalize Mathilda's journey into narcolepsy. Making sense of the why, to what end is anyone's suffering, I leave to the theologians and philosophers out there, my husband Oliver among them.

In the pages of this book you will not find answers to such questions. What you will read is the story of an unremarkable family who took incredible risks to ensure their survival. I want people to understand what happens in the lives of those whose children suffer with an incurable and debilitating condition. I want people to realize that although living with a child that has narcolepsy is an extraordinary experience, we are not extraordinary. And I want people to grasp that when adversity strikes at the heart of your family and your own heart, it is possible to light a candle in the desperate darkness of each night.

Narcolepsy has added another chapter to our lives. One that I have despised on more days than I care to remember. But one that I trust will resonate with all those that have endured the same crushing heartbreak of loving a child for whom you wish you could just take it all away. That my daughter suffers more than I do still seems wholly wrong to me, and yet deep within her soul, she is the same child I bore ten years ago, my child. Therefore it is incumbent upon me to tell her story as her mother—a story that we together share with millions of others.

With the exception of Dr. Siddarth Shah and Professor Emmanuel Mignot, I have changed the names of doctors, not wishing to expose those whom I believe did what they thought best for us as a family and for Mathilda—mighty in battle.

1 BRISTOL CHILDREN'S HOSPITAL
Spring 2010

> "I don't understand it any more than you do,
> but one thing I've learned is that you don't
> have to understand things for them to be."
>
> —**Madeline L'Engle**
> ***A Wrinkle In Time***

Early in the evening of April 15, 2010, Mathilda sways in the doorway of our bedroom, then locks her knees. With several slow blinks comes a sharp flick of her head, as if to wake herself before stumbling in our direction and promptly falling back to sleep between Oliver and me. Unconsciously she wets the bed. Her drowsiness has gripped her so tightly that she does not wake until the three of us are halfway through an assessment in the ER room at Bristol Children's Hospital. We tell the consultant about her excessive sleepiness during the day, the miserable waking and crying out through the night and the dramatic change in her personality. I explain she is also ataxic, has low tone, which she describes as feeling floppy and that, as an experienced physical therapist, I believe my daughter is neurologically sick on a fundamental level.

With one hand I wipe my face, then think over what I just said. I *was* a physical therapist, not more than being her mother, yet I know how the examination works and gently coax her to walk across the room for the "nice lady doctor." Mathilda slowly grumps away, staggering like a drunkard, holding out her arms to steady herself. Her steps, though intentional, are interrupted by a level of concentration she cannot hold. Once on my lap, the cold disc of the stethoscope against her chest jolts her back into the aseptic world of the ER room; she begins to cry and turns inward, nestling under my arm. I manage to keep Mathilda awake long enough for the doctor to shine a light into her eyes, test her reflexes and scrape the underside of her foot several times with the pointed end of the patella hammer. Moments later, her three-year old body is asleep again, and I feel a rising panic with the slow release of pee all over my lap. Yes, this is new. No, she never struggled with going to the bathroom independently. She had in fact been potty-trained for over a year. Oliver turns the doctor's attention from the wet patch spreading down my legs and fills the silence. Mathilda was always a bright and breezy child—sweet, funny, articulate, a real chatterbox with a *joie de vivre*. She had begun to read, but now was slurring her words and dropping off mid-sentence. Having returned home from a conference that weekend, Oliver could see the changes in his youngest child. He knows Mathilda isn't right—that these symptoms are hitting her hard and fast and that he, we, are both at a loss.

The doctor fails to wake her with tickles and the promise of new toys and friends in the play center upstairs. Gradually the tenor of our conversation changes, and I recognize that fixed look when doctors start to choose their words more carefully. We were "right to bring her in," and, "admission to the Neurology ward will be arranged immediately. The consultant neurologist and head of pediatric services may want to do an MRI on her brain. Tonight." I want to shake the doctor's sympathetic hand off my arm, aching from supporting Mathilda's seemingly lifeless body. I am so distracted by the singularity of meaning behind the doctors' words that, as if in a trance, I carry my daughter, floppy as a rag doll, and follow a young nurse to a bedded area behind the ER room. Distraught, I wait for admission and a bed on Ward 36.

Before our children were born, I worked only very briefly with pediatric patients when I was first qualified as a physical therapist. At West Middlesex Hospital in London, one of my duties was to reposition the ankles of club-footed babies and teach parents how to maintain the realignment I had achieved with strapping tape and stretches. Whatever their age or problem, I rarely had any trouble talking to patients. It was part of my training, part of my job, and part of me. The only time I had to reach deep down was when I rotated onto the intensive care unit as part of our post-graduate training, suctioning phlegm out of breathing tubes and stretching the limbs of the unconscious and those who reluctantly rapped at death's door. There is evidence to show that those near death can hear everything, yet on those days I felt self-conscious talking to monitors and never receiving a word back. I did what I could to promote the hope that belongs to every living soul, beginning my monologue and rhetoric over again most mornings on a unit full of new patients. But by the end of each long week, the turnover of patients was high enough to leave me emotionally wrung out and turning down offers for a night out on the town with friends. I was not cut out for it. After six months of crying at the end of each shift on intensive care and smiling at the beginning of the next one, I decided to move to orthopedics.

Mathilda was now lying on a hospital bed two miles away from our home in an overflow ward with half a dozen other children waiting to be transferred upstairs onto a ward. In a bed next to hers, a tube-fed older girl was either groaning or talking, I couldn't tell, whilst her mum ran a large brush through her thinning hair on the pillow. Her forearms were spindly and twisted across her chest, her fists contracted into tight balls under her chin.

"What's wrong with your little girl?" she asked me, a question that felt like a probe into something deeply personal.

"We don't know yet," I murmured, hoping it would close her down. She told me they lived somewhere between home and a range of hospitals, including Great Ormond Street in London and Bristol Children's, all the while trying to bring Rosie her daughter into the conversation, as if she would suddenly sit up and join in. Fearing she would draw comparisons between our daughters, I found myself struggling to articulate a response to her ongoing questions. But she was garrulous enough that I could get away with listening and throwing out the occasional platitude. She also had a very jolly disposition, despite her daughter's severe disability and normal results for every test imaginable. "How could all her brain scans be clear when she is like this?" she asked me. Rosie had seen specialists from all over the world and still needed 24-hour care.

Now, doctors were being flown in from Paris to assess her. They still had hope. Hope of understanding why their perfectly normal child had gradually regressed to a bedbound infant with a feeding tube and no intelligible language whilst her body passed through puberty. The only time I detected grief in the mother's voice was when she told me 40% of pediatric neurological cases remain undiagnosed in England, even after years of extensive testing. In my own mind, I trusted her figures were exaggerated and tried blowing them off; to have a declining child and no idea why was close to my worst nightmare. Caught somewhere between my past and this absurd present, I was suddenly alarmed by the thought that I was supposed to suction Rosie's tubes out and unbend her contracted knees. I imagined I would readjust her head, put her hands in splints to prevent further contractures and walk away. I could so easily have done that. But then I remembered I was on the other side of the fence now. And what a change that was. To go from knowledgeable to vulnerable, from clinician to patient, from happy to heartbroken. I wanted to switch back. And I wanted to take my baby home.

It was almost midnight when Dr. Anthony Jensen, consultant pediatric neurologist, and his team swept on to Ward 36. Mathilda was sleeping at the far end of a six-bedded bay beside a wall of glass, facing a city burning with streetlights and rattling with the constant peal of sirens. Oliver and I sat on either side of her bed, looking exhausted by the time the five doctors, hovering for a moment by the nurse's station, looked our way. Despite the late hour, there was an easiness about their presence as their hushed jokes belied the purpose of their visit. It seemed as though, after a long day, they had saved this new, straightforward case until last, and I felt myself relax into thinking things were not so serious. Doctor Jensen, a balding man in his forties, led his party towards the foot of the bed, dropping down by her feet covered by a green counterpane.

"This must be Mathilda. I'm Dr. Jensen, head of Pediatric Neurology. How's she doing?"

The open question led to vague answers about Mathilda, who was sleeping so soundly, one could have thought nothing was wrong with her. All she offered them was the shallow rise and fall of her chest and the skating of her eyeballs, like pendulums grafted beneath translucent eyelids.

During this exchange of questions and answers, Dr. Jensen ascertained that Oliver was a Reader in Philosophical Theology at the University of Bristol. They engaged in a conversation, which led to the realization that they were in fact colleagues. Dr. Jensen taught part-time at Bristol University Medical School, and their offices were just a few blocks away from each other. It was as though they had just been introduced at the university club over lunch, somewhere else, a million miles away from a sick child. And yet, I was not entirely unsympathetic to their effortless chumminess. A few moments' escape was intensely appealing—if only I could lift my eyes from the child between them.

With the four junior members of the team largely observing, Dr. Ellen Dimlock, the intern, stood some distance away, stroking the ear pieces of the stethoscope that she wore round her neck like a necklace. She was the only doctor in a white coat, which did little to hide her immaculate preppy clothes. I rose to shake her hand, sensing she wanted to nail specifics with me whilst Oliver and Dr. Jensen went on with their professional pleasantries. I listed Mathilda's symptoms for the second time that day: uncoordinated muscle movements (ataxia), slurring of sentences, pronounced daytime exhaustion, and the inability to sustain sleep either side of nightmares. I also relayed how she kept falling down whenever she tried to walk or play, that her personality was shifting, and that her latest symptom appeared to be incontinence. All this began, I said, around the same time as her collapse several weeks back, when a doctor at an ER Room on the South Coast diagnosed Mathilda with a urinary tract infection.

One of the young house doctors, who I later came to know as Rafael, went off to find a patella hammer, a basic piece of medical equipment for any neurologist in any hospital. He returned several minutes later with a nurse fumbling an apology. There did not seem to be one in the ward. Since none of the doctors carried one either, Dr. Jensen made light of resources being scarce in the National Health

Service, a comment that sent further ripples of laughter amongst the team. Then, cutting in as if to reign in an unruly pack, he said:

"I've had a chat with the ER doctor who admitted Mathilda this evening. I don't think we need to worry about waking her and performing another neurological exam now. The clinical picture here seems pretty clear. She's an excellent doctor and I have no reason to doubt her judgment." Then, just as the screeching of sirens outside stilled, Dr. Jensen dropped a bomb. "I am not going to bullshit you," he said, lifting his head, his hands clasped together. "We're looking at a cerebellar tumor."

Brain tumors that lie between the brain stem and cerebrum typically afflict a person with drowsiness, unsteady gait, ataxia and personality changes. This was partly consistent with Mathilda's symptoms, and the immediate MRI under anesthesia was expected to confirm the diagnosis of a malignant lesion. Dr. Jensen, so confident in his colleague's earlier assessment, asked the on-call radiologist to let him know, at home in the small hours, the precise locale of Mathilda's tumor. Standing there shaking, I simultaneously tried to process what he had just said whilst grasping on to key words he threw out, like biopsy, chemotherapy and treatment options down the road. Yet by the time I had ordered my train of thoughts to form anything like a coherent question, he and his team were gone.

Oliver drew the curtains around Mathilda's bed and held me very close for a long time, saying nothing. His towering height and strong arms went some way to assure me that, even in the event of malignancy, together, in one piece, as one unit, we would get through the impending threat to our child's brain. Screening out the commotion in the ward, the nurses talking in the drug room, and the lively conversations issuing from several TV sets, he finally drew back and raised the safe issue of practical arrangements. It was a given that I would stay, the one who spoke the language of hospitals, and that he, terrified of them, would go back to our older children, Liberty and Elliot. Yet even the thought of our regular lives at home, the kids sleeping in their bunk beds with toys strewn across the room, couldn't reel me in from what lay ahead. And his love for us, however deep, would reach only so far. It could not actually change the facts, certainly would not alter what showed up on the MRI. Neither of us, as parents, professionals, or anything else, could erase her symptoms or lessen her suffering. This realization of utter powerlessness left me feeling as if we were failing our child, giving rise to a sense that the entire situation was unnatural, perhaps even theatrical. There must be some explanation for the aberrance in what was unfolding. It was not right. Any of it.

Despite the surreality of the situation, I could not reconcile my sense of injustice with the fact that every ward at Bristol Children's Hospital was full wall-to-wall. A 160 bedded regional unit, that meant 160 sick children. And what of the others? The dozens in the ER room and the overflow ward? The children in different hospitals, different countries? The war I began to wage on myself that night against my own rationalization of suffering left me oscillating between our neurological demise and the simple question— why *not* us? Never did I expect to dodge all the bullets of ill health. But when they came, it seemed like a firing squad had let rip on my heart.

I understood that Mathilda, like every other child in the hospital, was at the mercy of God, who, if He so desired, could wipe the brain scan clear and return her to us by breakfast. She was also at the mercy of the doctors who would go on caring for her long after the MRI was done. In my own my mind, I had begun to acknowledge that whatever was wrong with her was here to stay. It was an intuition that came at me with a maternal gravity that I had, up until that point, never before encountered. Then, facing the most frightening few hours of my life, I watched Oliver bend over Mathilda, whisper a prayer of his own, and just as the team had done half an hour earlier, walk away.

Leaving Mathilda asleep, I went in search of a phone.

My parents have always maintained an etiquette regarding the appropriate use of the landline, stipulating that, under normal circumstances, nobody should make or receive a call after 9 p.m. Ringing later than that signified something terrible—an impending disaster or a death. This courtesy I upheld even when I went into labor. A number of babies are prone to arrive in the small hours; mine were no exception. Not wishing to deprive my parents of a night's sleep we left the good news until morning and called after 9 a.m. Even now unable to break the familial protocol, I rang my sister Amanda instead, and as soon as she picked up, I broke down. Standing at the nurse's station and sobbing into the handset, I listened to the steadiness in her voice.

"Claire, you don't know that yet. You don't know what's wrong with her until the scan comes back. Stay with the facts. And right now the facts are that Mathilda is in good hands, and as far as you know, she *doesn't* have a brain tumor."

Stay with the facts. Stay with the facts. I replayed her words like a chant. Crawling near the cot-bed between Mathilda and the cold wall, I offered up my own petition: that God would spare her, that there would be no brain tumor, no disease at all. My words blurred into one long plaintive plea. I knew better than to bargain with the Deity, but I did it anyway. If He would loosen the grip of neurological disaster, I would no longer doubt Him. There would not be a cell in my body that would question His hand on her life. From that moment on I would have absolute, un-wavering confidence in His mercy. I would do a better job at everything, be a better parent, a better person. I lay on my side, looking across at Mathilda in agonizing self-exam-ination. My mind cast all the way back to the many mis-takes I had made, trying to rationalize which misdemeanors would add up to her being there. I knew that was not really how it worked, that I was not thinking along straight lines, but I could not help myself. Trawling through my child-hood, teens and early adulthood, I realized that it was not so much that I had done something terribly wrong; I had simply asked for too much. Three healthy children. That was it. Mathilda, our third child, had tipped some kind of theological balance.

Down in the empty basement of the hospital at 2 a.m., I continued stroking her face until she was wheeled off past the markings on the floor strictly stating, "Beyond this point, no access to parents." I found the one empty waiting area and sat on a black plastic chair, staring at cinder blocks and a shelf of beat-up children's books. Nothing marked the minutes except the drum beat of a headache pounding in time with the shrill beeping sounds coming from the scan-ning machine working over Mathilda's head a few rooms away. I pressed my thighs down firmly on my hands to stop them trembling. *Stay with the facts. Stay with the facts until they tell you otherwise.* The truth lay somewhere between the long small hours of the night, my own exhaustion, and the threat of losing her.

It was right then and there that I had the strong sense that the two of us were being dangled over a gaping abyss. It may have been a vision, although by then I was already deep into months of sleep deprivation; I could not be sure. Yet the image was crystal clear, and it would return to me in varying degrees over the months that followed.

During the forty or so minutes that Mathilda underwent the MRI, I could see myself, as if observing from a distance, holding onto a rope above with one hand and firmly gripping Mathilda's forearm with the other. Below us was a black cavern, empty and threatening; high above us was a cliff top that was too far up to be reached. I was exposed, fighting a fear that shook me so violently I wondered if God Himself was pulling me, testing the grip of my hands. If I let go, we would both fall. I would lose it all. I would question everything I believed in—goodness, purpose, meaning. He was the hurricane that blew around me, dangling there that night, and He became the tempest that, over the next few years, would threaten our survival. I was alone and terrified.

In the isolation and bareness of that space, staring at the bleak uncertainties ahead, I stopped bargaining and spared myself the burden of trying to make sense of it all. And with

Mathilda clinging to my arm, I made a calculated decision: *To not let go.*

2 NEW FOREST
June 2005-January 2006

> "You can't sit in your corner of the forest
> waiting for others to come to you. You
> have to go to them sometimes."

> —**A.A. Milne**
> ***Winnie The Pooh***

If I'd known Oliver's new career as a scholar in pursuit of tenure would require us to move house, country, and continent with two infants over the next five years, I might have challenged his first post in St. Andrews, Scotland. Securing short-term contracts as a teaching fellow, as well as publishing his PhD thesis and papers in prestigious journals, required the skill set of not just the *uber*-intelligent but also the nomad. The latter required an emotional tenacity for which I was unprepared and found extremely unsettling. I had always loved his energy and determination to live every day as if it was his last. Yet having been raised largely in one locality with my extended family a few blocks away, I had no reference points for this bedouin lifestyle and no real desire for it. Since attending the University of Aberdeen as an undergraduate, he had stacked up five concurrent years in Postgraduate studies (MTh from Aberdeen and PhD at King's College, London), three years as a high school teacher and another three as an assistant Pastor. I, on the other hand, had trained and worked in London hospitals for the better part of ten years, continuing my profession by working in a private practice in the evenings whilst caring for our two young children in between packing and unpacking the few tangible objects that make a house a home. In our case, that was Oliver's library, the kids' toys and a handful of my grandmother's pots and pans.

The two years we spent in Scotland from 2002-2004 were hard. It was hard to live with the uncertainty of a renewed nine-month contract as a humble teaching fellow in Theology when Oliver was distracted up in the ivory tower trying to forge an impressive résumé that would secure professional and financial security in the future. It was also hard to find affordable housing, and to opt for value bread at Tesco over vegetables and sanitary towels. I spent the better part of those days with Liberty and Elliot, wading in rock pools along the low tides of East and West Sands, bringing the shells they collected back in buckets to our apartment. As I saw it, my job was to somehow immunize them from the worries which kept Oliver and I awake and distant from one another.

We talked quietly at night of what was next and how we would make it work. Never did we let the other know where our fears really lay. We were pulling together as a team, just as we had convinced the children we were in fact on an intentional family adventure. Oliver internalized his fears of failing, working long hours at St. Mary's College. There were good times there with friends, mostly American PhD students who, like us, were passing through the ancient town with their young families on a wing and a prayer. But it ended abruptly in the very last week of the year, with Oliver and Elliot in surgery at the same time in Ninewells Hospital, and with no renewed contract. Then, just as suddenly as St. Andrew's door closed, another opened. So, whilst I nursed Elliot through ear surgery and Oliver through back surgery, I learned how to up and pack at a moment's notice. Only this time with fewer tears.

Accepting the Frederick J. Crosson Research Fellowship at the University of Notre Dame in Indiana was an exciting opportunity, even if I'd never been to the US before. Neither of us had the slightest idea of what a Midwest winter looked like, nor what lay beyond those ten months. But with the publication of a second book, it would be a year that significantly shaped Oliver's career. It was also one wherein we consolidated our resolve to swim against the educational tide by educating Liberty and Elliot ourselves. We needed to limit the impact our itinerant lifestyle was having on them; pulling them in and out of schools seemed wrong and unfair. In designing our own curriculum, we felt we could allow them the opportunity of growing and learning at their own pace, away from social pressure and popular culture, even if it meant embarking on an academic route that was outside the box. What we did not realize, however, was that both children would not set foot in an academic institution for the next six years, and only then because the decision was taken out of our hands.

After a year at Notre Dame, we drifted back to the UK in the summer of 2005, with our two young children and our professional tails dragging limply between our legs. The many jobs for which Oliver had interviewed that year, both in the US and UK, had come to nothing. Despite the string of qualifications, degrees, publications and professional experience, we were both officially unemployed, disillusioned, and broke. Were it not for my parents owning a tiny and spectacularly cute, Victorian cottage in the heart of the New Forest, we would also have found ourselves homeless.

To say that we lived simply is an understatement. It felt as though we had gone back in time, sometimes a bit too far back. The country lane we lived on outside Lyndhurst was lined with mostly detached homes that were over two hundred years old. Some were thatched, adorned with climbing roses and utterly un-spoilt. One in particular was so quintessentially English that it could have been found in the village newsstand on a postcard, along with images of ponies in streams and other woodland scenes.

Most evenings on our last walk of the day we waved to an elderly neighbor, who worked so consistently between his rows of potatoes and brussels sprouts that we named him Mr. McGregor, from Beatrix Potter's stories. Only he was friendly towards the children and never ate rabbit. By dusk, the gardens would fill up with dozens of Peters and Benjamins and all sizes of Flopsy bunnies, hopping through the picket fences, their white tails lifting in the moonlight. It was the only time we experienced living in a place untouched by industrialization, immune somehow from man's invasion on nature and almost entirely intact. So rich and abundant was our environment that it was not difficult to exist within its rhythms, keeping time with the seasons and allowing it to provide us with all manner of comforts. We would read in glades, wade in rivers and lose ourselves in the forest's tranquility. With the slow arrival of winter, the fallen branches found their way onto our wood burner, which heated all four rooms well into the small hours. By morning the embers receded, and off we went, wrapped up and ready to collect more wood for another day.

Soon after being rejected for unemployment benefit on the grounds of having not lived in the UK for the past year, despite the previous ten as fully-fledged taxpayers, the four of us took to foraging in the forest where we lived. In addition to firewood, it provided us with fruit, and hours of recreation. We began to recognize the wild horses, pigs and deer as our very own woodland companions. To this day our children can identify almost every English tree there is. Liberty, in particular, named some of the ponies that wandered about outside our cottage, looking for them on waking and whenever we came home from an errand. Fortuitously, the benefits of living in a welfare state did not elude us entirely. Our family was deemed poor enough to be awarded milk coupons and free eye tests, of all things. The eagerly anticipated daily rounds of the milk float became one of the highlights of our afternoons. When John the milkman in the white coat and cap pulled up the lane, he would cheerfully throw in a loaf of bread or a bun round along with our daily four pints of milk. Maybe he took pity on our sweet children with their endless curiosity and grinning faces. Or perhaps he had noticed we were all losing weight. Either way, we all really liked that man.

Six months into our explorations in the forest and playing Pooh sticks at Robin Hood bridge not far from the cottage, three things happened. And all were good. An interview for a permanent position in Theology at the University of Bristol was on the cards. We had decided that if the appointing committee had an agenda and the post was biased towards an inside applicant, as the previous four had been, it was high time to throw the academic towel in and accept that our years of risk-taking had backfired. Living in the New Forest without a job between us meant we were fast running out of resources. And with Oliver's email inbox steadily drying up we had begun to think earnestly about other options. With plenty of hospitals and schools around, I could return to physiotherapy and Oliver could go back to high school teaching. The accumulated doubt and lowered expectations of employed life persuaded me to join him on the day of his interview, something I had never felt necessary before. Our best man, Peter Wood, came to look after the children whilst Oliver and I set out for the densely populated streets of Bristol city center. We both knew this was it—a turning point that would determine either tenure, or a serious re-thinking of our future. It's no exaggeration to say that the rain poured hard and long that day, as if to cast an ominous spell over the University. Still, somewhere between his remaining fragments of hope and the prayers I muttered, there was enough left in us both to believe this position might be his.

Pulling up outside the Theology department building, I leaned over and kissed Oliver, wishing him all the luck in the world and what felt like a trite pep talk on succeeding when I knew he felt professionally washed up. Then I parked and started out for the provincial museum until I realized I had left both my purse and umbrella back at the cottage. I settled on a couch at the University Club instead, took refuge from the rain and waited it out.

Sometime after the second interview, I heard the high-pitched tone of the walkie-talkie. With only one cell phone between us we had grabbed Elliot's hand held two-way radio so Oliver could contact me between the rounds of interviews. It took us both several minutes to find a spot where we could pick up a reception without being interrupted by other people's conversations across the sound waves. So desperate was I for good news I blew off the embarrassment I might have registered when academics threw strange glances my way as I called into what was clearly a four-year-old's handset.

"Where are you? Over."

"Outside the Club. Actually opposite you. How is it going? Over."

"Interesting. Over."

"What do you mean interesting? Over."

"I think this is the first time that it's a level playing field. Over."

"That's brilliant. So you think you have chance?"

"Over? You're breaking up."

"Yes. Yes. Over."

"Maybe. I'm not sure. There's an Oxbridge candidate and two others. I'll have to go. Over." My heart sank at the thought of stiff competition. He'd already lost out to Oxbridge candidates in previous interviews.

"Okay. Good luck with the next round. This job is yours. I'm sure of it. Over."

"You okay? Over."

"Fine. A little wet. And hungry. Maybe we can grab supper later? Over."

"Yes. They've already said they'd let the successful candidate know tonight. Whatever happens, let's stop on our way back for something to eat. Over and out."

Later that evening, we sat opposite each other in Rajpoot, a curry house with views across Bath Abbey, trying to rationalize why someone from the interviewing panel had not called. Oliver was spent. The day had squeezed all reserves out of him, leaving him blank and wearing the disappointment of a man whose ideals and efforts of the past ten years had been washed away. I wanted to buoy him up, keep it all alive for him, but everything I could think of seemed like pathetic sound bites from a self-help manual. My hopes were too entwined with his, and he was feeling much too disillusioned.

I cannot remember how long we waited—silence pregnant with anticipation drags out time and misshapes it. But in one moment Oliver went from zero to hero after what seemed like an eternity of trying to prove himself worthy of the ivory tower. By the time our cell phone vibrated on the table I was close to the edge. He simply stared at it before flicking open the lid. The only thing to come out of his mouth was a weak *hello*. I could hear a man's voice, positive at first, then confused. Gavin D'Costa, the Professor heading the appointing committee, repeated himself twice. *Did he want the job?* Oliver was stunned to a point of silence; it was all I could do not to reach across the table, grab the phone with my heart in my throat and do the talking for him. I will never forget the look of disbelief on Oliver's face, and I cannot recall another time when he has so struggled to articulate his thoughts. Whilst they exchanged words, I gave myself permission to cry into the oversized yellow napkin and let go of the weighted worry of unemployment. The full-time, permanent position as a lecturer at the University of Bristol was quite literally a godsend, and when Providence smiles upon you like that, you enjoy it.

The second fortuitous event occurred just a few weeks later. The four of us had driven to a housing estate on the far west side of Bristol city called Pill to look at a house. We all squeezed into our black Ford Ka, a very compact car that Liberty had affectionately named "Putt-Putt." You could just about fit two small children in the back, each with a bag on their lap, or in Elliot's case, a potty. But we had a lot for which to thank Putt-Putt. He was reliable, affordable, and the main reason our young children walked miles and miles. No stroller was made small enough to fit in the miniature trunk, no matter how much you tried to wedge it in.

As we were leaving one of these Lego-like kit houses which took less than ten minutes to look over, a couple opposite us backed their oversized BMW out of their driveway, and did not stop until they hit Putt-Putt, crumpling the entire length of the rear panel. Even more distressing than watching our only means of transport folding on one side was what followed from the front passenger, who leapt out towards us, hurling abuse bluer than anything our children had ever heard before. The four of us stood rooted on the sidewalk, stunned at being blamed, and distracted by the knowledge that we had no way of replacing or repairing Putt-Putt. He was our most valuable material possession, and whilst we had never really cared for the status cars can bring, it was genuinely upsetting to think we would now have no means of finding a home by Christmas.

As it turned out, however, the couple favored a cash settlement over claiming on their insurance. We could either spend the £1000 to make Putt-Putt beautiful again or drive him around battered and bruised and bank the money. It took many more visits to Bristol to find our home in a place on the North side, far, far away from Pill, but the financial provision garnered from the crash that morning lasted us right up to the week we finally moved. Putt-Putt was the only car that ever put food on the table, and it was another sign that a benevolent deity was smiling on us.

Our last few weeks in the New Forest were spent relishing country life whilst planning to move to the big city. It made sense to keep home-schooling Liberty and Elliot. The primary spoken language at our new local school in Bristol was Urdu, and neither of them had so much as completed level one French. Besides, they were thriving. Once again, we spoke of our next family adventure, only this time Oliver and I really believed it. We had cooked and eaten every meal together, walked and talked for hours in the New Forest without any other adult to question our shelving away of the unspoken fears that once threatened to isolate us. Heartened by a fresh found enthusiasm for life and a strong desire to create something new, we gathered up the children's many books and toys, and hired a van, which we would soon drive Westward.

It was around this same time that I began to crave one thing above everything else—oranges. At first, we both wondered if it was my body's way of telling me I needed to stop overdosing on bread and milk provided by John the milkman. But as Oliver filled the weekly Tesco trolley with more vitamin C than pasta, and indulged me on the day of our move in frequent motorway stops where I could throw up in the luxury of fresh air, I realized that the English saying about moving into a new home with a new baby was true. I was pregnant.

3 MATHILDA
Spring-Summer 2006

> "When the first baby laughed for the first time, its laugh broke into a thousand pieces, and they all went skipping about and that was the beginning of fairies."

> **—J.M. Barrie**
> ***Peter Pan***

The first half of 2006 was a reasonably quiet and stable period for our family. We settled into our new home and community, and I began to relax into my third pregnancy, filling each day with the home education of Liberty and Elliot. Oliver began teaching at the University of Bristol, easing into the security that a permanent job offered. He wrote and taught classes, gained his first PhD student, and was drafted into various administrative committees. Such was his fear of being unemployed again that he also maintained a steady publishing pace, writing articles and books long into the night. As with all British universities, there was a culture of '*publish or perish,*' which hangs over every young academic's career like the proverbial Sword of Damocles. He finally had a job, and he wanted to keep it.

The house we bought sat on the north side of the city in

Stapleton, once a real village until it was sliced in half by the M32, the main artery out of the city center. Built in 1936 with four bedrooms (two were box rooms), and a garage not wide enough for Putt-Putt, our semi-detached home was the first we had owned in seven years. Looking out from our back bedroom window, to the left was a 200-foot church spire and a 15th century dry-stone wall marking the end of our garden. To the right was one of the city's most noticeable landmarks, a communications tower perched on a hill and flanked on all sides with over-sized satellite dishes. This all but summed up Bristol for me: beautiful *and* unsightly.

A handful of midwives in our new neighborhood provided obstetric care. They all insisted that the third baby always came late, and always came slow. At the age of thirty-six, technically speaking I was a geriatric mother, and with two pregnancies already behind me, I was also considered experienced. I had no doubt the baby would come quickly. Neither did Oliver, who'd already witnessed my two previous precipitate labors, leaving him with the burdensome realization that this time he might literally be left holding the baby. The midwife designated to my delivery, an elderly lady called Annie, made it clear from the start that without blue lights and sirens in her car, she'd never make it across the congested streets of Bristol within forty minutes. I understood that, but I also knew that if she didn't make it to me in time, I wouldn't make it to hospital either for the same reasons. My worst fear was not Oliver being unqualified to deliver a baby, but his actually not being there. If I was the only adult in the house, how would I hide the mess of it all from a six and four-year-old? I had no idea how I would reach down and deliver a baby when I couldn't see past my own navel, let alone go looking for the phone.

"There's no way I'm doing that." He said one night after work. "What do you mean Annie won't make it here once we've called? It's her job."

"I'm only telling you what she told me today. That none of the midwives can guarantee getting to us in under an hour." I responded. "They might, but they might not."

"I can't deliver a baby, Claire. It's not only that I don't want to. It's dangerous."

"Then let's book into the hospital. It's what, two miles away?" I knew what was coming next.

"You won't make it. You'll have the baby in the car," he said, dialing through to the antenatal clinic I had just returned from. I heard him express his concern, his voice escalating as he pressed the fact that he had already seen me in labor twice and on both occasions the babies were born in less than an hour. But Annie's voice at the end of the line countered, and something in her tone persuaded him to listen carefully to her coaching. I saw him taking notes.

"Mobile number is 0117-678-9953. Get Claire to bear

down, make sure the cord is not round the baby's neck, and whatever you do, don't cut it. Wait until I arrive. Don't call 9-9-9. Home deliveries are a waste of their time."

With there being hardly any point to writing out a birth plan, we indulged ourselves in the delightful task of choosing our baby's name. This time round, I had final say. Several years back, my sister, who looked to remain both single and childless, had chosen the name of our son, Elliot. Which we loved. Prior to that, Oliver felt that his first child had released him from the pain of a depression-filled season immediately following a miscarriage I had not long after we were married. We both dealt with the subsequent period of loss and confusion in different ways. He wrestled with his demons and doubts by writing a thesis on the problem of suffering and sent it off a year later to Aberdeen University. They granted him a Master's degree for it. I went back to work, treating minor injuries, mobilizing elderly patients in a village hospital, and, with a heavy heart, attending christenings of friends' newborns on the weekends.

By the time Liberty arrived, I had a list of names ready, such as Imogen or Isabelle, Cressida and Hermione, all of which, as a teenager, she now squirms at. When Oliver leaned her squashed up face into my red one, he *knew* what we should call her. "*Liberty*," he said through the tears, "because she has set me free." I understood what he was saying, and yet I offered up my pathetic list before letting it go. In that moment it was impossible to argue with a man who, in the silence of the hospital room, allowed his firstborn to dissolve years of internal disquiet. Babies can do that. Theology cannot.

Knowing ahead of time that our third child was a girl, it was easy for me to settle on the name Mathilda, which literally translates as "mighty in battle," or "little fighter." Oliver agreed that there was a ring of nobility to it, a certain strength. And since neither of us were superstitious, trusted omens or thought her name was in anyway a forewarning, we chose it regardless. It was simply a beautiful name with a beautiful meaning.

Three weeks ahead of schedule, I woke feeling oppressed by a rare heat wave that was suffocating the UK and a general malaise one usually associates with the flu. I was due to drive Wendy, a new friend I had made through home schooling, and her girls Hannah and Heather, to a pottery class across town. Oliver ended up calling her to swap weeks instead. Almost as soon as he handed the kids over at the front door, I stood up from my bed, and underneath my shiny belly saw thighs that were streaked with thin lines of grey meconium. Baby poop. Worse than that, I could no longer feel any fetal movement, however much I pleaded with my baby to boot her tiny feet into a rib or two.

Feeling strangely sleepy and already disconnected from what was about to take place, I calmly called for Oliver to come. The slow guttural tone of my voice had him leaping up the stairs, with the phone in one hand and a piece of paper with numbers on it in the other. He seemed almost comical, looking deadly serious, and wearing an ill-fitting T-shirt with Liberty and Elliot's handprints painted across his chest. In red cursive were the words, *"Best Daddy hands down."* The two of them had made it for him just a few weeks back on Father's Day.

Reaching back to that morning, I can see how the next few minutes might have played out as a scene from a hospital drama. As predicted, we were alone. I sensed Oliver's panicked attempt to control the situation, first directing me, then speaking to a voice at the end of the line: *I can see the baby's head-take off your knickers-these towels and plastic sheets won't work—move to the bathroom-stand in the bath—scan the sheet slowly for the midwife's number—go downstairs and prop the front door open with something—she will come soon-but not soon enough—call 999—-hurry—we live at 17 The Chine Bristol—it's my wife—run back upstairs—take deep breaths—you need to push down now Claire—now—get a towel—we need an ambulance—yes there is clear street access—block out the blood and the poop—my wife is giving birth—open the window, it's too hot—get a towel—I am alone with my wife—push harder—the baby is coming out—I have*

her—I have the baby—what do I do?—Operator, I need an
ambulance!—What do I do?—The baby is blue—She isn't
breathing—what do I do?

Oliver appeared so small of a sudden. He was below
me crying. The phone wedged between his right shoulder
and ear holding a blue baby in a blue towel, confessing to
the woman on the end of the line, and willing his words to
push air into his daughter's lungs.

"I am doing my best, I am doing my best. She's not
breathing."

"Sir. You're doing fine. Hold the baby face down and
slap her on her back. Slap her back hard."

"I am, I am. She's not breathing. Yes I am slapping her."

"Is she breathing at all?"

"No. She's not breathing. I am trying my best. When
will help be here?"

"They are on their way. Is your wife okay?

"No. Yes. She's okay. The baby is blue. She is not moving."

"Is the baby still attached to the cord?"

"Yes. The cord. The cord is in the bath. It's very long."

"Keep slapping the baby firmly on the back until she
takes a breath. Don't cut the cord."

"I'm doing my best. I'm doing my best. It's not working!"

"Paramedics are on their way. They will be with you

very soon. Keep the baby face down. You are doing really well Mr. Crisp. Just keep on slapping her back hard."

I wish I could say that I helped them both, but it was all I could do to keep my fists fixed to the shower rail, resist the centrifugal urge to collapse down where there were other parts of me, and succumb to the rotating room and the pull of what seemed like deep sleep. I wanted to reach out and hold her before drifting beyond the bathroom walls, out to the garden where birds were singing in the climbing heat. Mathilda was the color of a peacock I thought, her body reflecting the blue towel in which she was wrapped. All would be well if it were white, and the two of us could rest a while. She just needed a white towel. Why couldn't Oliver let us both rest instead of shaking her and sobbing?

He was holding the limp infant entirely in the cup of his left hand, her arms dangling downward as if reaching for the phone he had dropped. I tried to speak, but the words did not come, circling around the inside of my head against a low-grade humming. I went on feeling as though I was being dragged backwards through a cool tunnel, out of the room and away from the thick air and the agonizing pleas of a desperate man. Only the rising waves of nausea, the pool of blood and bits against the white bath reminded me where I was. I focused all my strength on straightening my knees. If I could keep them from giving out, I could stay awake. In the distance Oliver was whispering promises of her childhood to come, imploring her to hold on. She would love the beach. Her brother and sister wanted to meet her. Her mum and dad had a lifetime of love for her. God loved her. We all loved her. *Breathe, baby. Please. Breathe.* I leaned against the cool tiles to steady the vibrations behind my eyes and hung onto the words he whispered in her ear, unable to tell if any of it was real or not.

In actual time it was 9 a.m. We were only about seven minutes into the delivery from Annie's arrival when I was jolted back into the room, hearing Oliver yelling, "We are up here. You're too late for the birth, but we need your help!" Appearing instantly in the bathroom she grabbed Mathilda, tipping her upside down and thumping life into her. Whether she knew better than to question a distraught father or genuinely sensed the danger in that room, I don't know. But I saw her just a few feet away, standing by the sink, wearing a black backpack and whacking our baby so hard her six-pound spine could have snapped. Some primeval instinct finally kicked in. Mathilda choked, then gasped. She spluttered her way through the next few breaths until she drew in enough air to let out a cry. She cried as hard as any newborn, then, breaking the silence and scattering our sense of foreboding into tiny fragments and bittersweet memories.

Two paramedics arrived in time to hand Mathilda to Oliver and distract him from what was next. I found myself on our bed, listening to the banter of men's voices against the midwives' exchanges, weaving in and around the room. I remember thinking that Mathilda must be alive and well if people were laughing from somewhere in the house, though I could not quite place where. Much later, Oliver shared that there had been joking about his T-shirt. Both paramedics, in a west-country brogue, insisted he had worn it intentionally, knowing he was about to prove himself the *best Dad, hands down*. I doubt he had the strength to laugh, but a photo they took of him shows him wan and smiling, holding Mathilda close to his chest, her waxy head between two child-sized handprints.

My senses came reeling into sharp focus as I felt an acute piercing in the lower half of my body. I was naked, lying on my back, and could see that Annie was gloved and moving between my legs. Another midwife pinned my shoulders against the pillows, telling me it would be over soon if only I would lie still. Close by, Oliver was also being held back. The paramedics insisted he let them do their job, despite my blood curdling cries begging them to stop, to wait. Wait until I could cope. I needed a moment for the pain to subside, a moment to breathe, to bear what the midwives were doing. I heard the two women mention a large tear, and the removal of everything that should have been delivered. The internal examination continued, involving hands and instruments, and unbearable pain until I reached the point of blacking out.

If that July morning could be re-written, I would have asked for pain relief, or time to pace myself and slow it all down. I would have spared Oliver the trauma of trying to bring our daughter round with nothing more than his own two hands, holding her life right there in the balance. The two of us might have looked closely at the fragility of our lives, the marriage that held it all together, and braced ourselves for what lay ahead instead of basking in relief at the cool end of that day. Or perhaps after the birth we would have paused time, locking ourselves into the deepening sunset and the wonderment that filled all five of us when Liberty and Elliot came home and met their sister.

As for Mathilda, I am certain I would have offered an alternative to being born into the hands of parents who, in the same moment, knew both terror and trust, and were entirely dependent on something outside of themselves. I would have gone before her, honoring that unspoken contract we have with our children when they are born, to lead them on a path well-trod, to show them the delights of the world first-hand, but its dangers from a distance. Above all, I would have re-ordered the next few days, months and years of her life, of all our lives, and measured out the hardship so it was enough to prepare them for their futures, but not so much that we would sink under their weight.

Looking back, I am caught up in gratitude for us both making it through that day, and, albeit briefly, for the rhythms of life that followed—rhythms that mark time with the laughter and endless questions of children, and that bind lovers beneath the cover of joyful devotion. That night, after envisioning the five of us around our large dining table and putting each of the children to bed with their songs, stories and worries, my body finally gives way to the one thing that would, soon enough, elude and haunt Mathilda, mighty in battle—sleep.

4 BREATHING
July 2006-Summer 2008

"Let the wild rumpus start."

—**Maurice Sendak**
Where the Wild Things Are

All the rest of that first day was filled with visitors. Neighbors came with gifts and claimed to have not heard a word, only seen the ambulance parked outside our house for a few hours earlier. My friend Wendy dropped Liberty and Elliot back home, and late into the afternoon we had a visit from Dr. Bledsoe, our family physician. A family man with a lighthearted manner, he brought with him a young medical student, looking more like a high school student than someone to whom you would trust the health of your newborn. They appeared without notice in my bedroom where I was drifting in and out of sleep, Mathilda swaddled beside me in a Moses basket. Looking up at the two of them smartly dressed and smiling down at the baby, I grabbed my robe and covered up before arranging my face.

"How are you?" he asked lightly.

"Oh. Pretty good," I replied, lifting upwards in the bed and biting down on sweeping shocks of pain.

"So we need to run through a basic examination. Routine when a baby is born at home. You've had quite a morning."

"We certainly did. Mathilda surprised us. I think Oliver's still in shock."

"This one's a little sweetheart," he went on, unwrapping Mathilda from the muslin cloth with a familiarity that was somewhat unsettling. Despite my primordial achievement that morning, I could not shrug off feelings close to shame. Sitting there in the stifling heat, half draped in my large white fluffy robe, a Christmas gift from my mum that I hadn't the heart to tell her I didn't like. Why had I never invested in something more streamlined? Something made of natural fibers and that didn't make me drip with sweat. At some point Oliver came in and gave me an ice pack to sit on. Lifting onto it was no small achievement. The medical student stood poised with her notebook and pen, meeting my gaze smiling in my direction. Her presence only added to my sense of awkwardness, and when Dr. Bledsoe, sensing my discomfort, asked if it was all right for her to be there, I came very close to saying no. Sometime after checking Mathilda's vital signs and advising me on how to deal with her jaundice, he turned her around, removed the tiny diaper and said, "Last but not least we have to make sure there is a hole." I watched them both peer into Mathilda's rear end and declare her to be an altogether healthy specimen, if a little on the small side. It felt like they were playing a game, one which I might even have joined had I not been preoccupied with hiding the milk that dripped, as if from a faulty faucet, and was now leaking through the bed-clothes.

Several days later, I climbed the stairs to check on Mathilda. She was sleeping in a crib in her room, from which a striking, squeaking sound issued, heard clear to the foot of the stairs. Carried over the low hum of the fan, Mathilda let out high-pitched rasping noises, not unlike a plastic whistle you might find in a cheap Christmas cracker. I scooped her up immediately. The noise settled. I put her down. The rasping kicked in again. When I undressed her, her rib cage sank in with each breath, as did the hollow notch in the nape of her neck.

"Oliver! Come and see this!" He was within earshot across the landing in his study.

"Look at her breathing. It's not right," I said, trying to push down the inevitable panic.

"I've never seen that before," he replied. "What is wrong with her?"

"She sounds like a bird. She's squeaking." I picked her up again to stop it. As soon as I lay her back down, it started all over again, only this time her chest began heaving on inhalation, her tiny abdomen sucking and bloating with a pulse all of its own.

Long into the night in the ER room at Bristol Children's Hospital, Mathilda was subject to a chest X-Ray, various blood tests and a lumbar puncture. For Oliver, the sterilized smells and the sight of staff in uniforms drew out his deepest fears, despite working as a hospital porter years back when he was home from college. In the summer of 1993, just weeks before our wedding, he managed to find a couple of months' work at the same hospital in West London in which he had been born. Coincidently, I was already working there, on a six-month orthopedic rotation. At the absolute bottom of the food chain, he was assigned to moving bodies between the ER room, the CCU (coronary care unit), and the freezer drawers of the morgue, where his job was to arrange the bodies for distraught relatives to identify.

I was a newly qualified physical therapist working hard to teach hip replacement patients how to go up and down stairs on crutches without damaging anything before being given consent for their discharge. On occasion, Oliver and I passed each in the long hospital corridors, both dressed in uniforms that disguised our engagement. Only if you caught us winking from a distance or driving off together at the end of our shifts would you know we were lovers. It was not what you would call a typical summer job, and it left him distrustful of hospitals and fearful when he faced his own back surgeries years later. For me, working in hospitals and in Primary Care facilities gave me confidence to navigate almost any clinical situation. Or so I thought.

Suspecting that Mathilda could be brewing an infection internally on account of her meconium delivery and high temperature, the junior ER doctor advised us to consent to an immediate lumbar puncture. It was true that she was hot, but I argued that we were all hot. The room was roasting. Despite the late hour, the red bricks of Bristol Children's Hospital had retained the July heat, and without windows or air conditioning, the ER room lay deep within the heart of the hospital like a tomb—airless. Following the chest x-ray and blood work that had both come back as normal, we were ushered into a side room, sparsely furnished with a few wall-mounted cupboards, a sink and a stainless steel bench in the center. I assumed the procedure would be performed under anesthesia of some kind and with a senior doctor supervising the newly qualified one. But the absence of medical colleagues meant it fell on me to pin Mathilda on her side, curled up in a fetal position, for the five attempts in forty-five minutes it took the young doctor to extract spinal fluid with a needle. She was so small that her two ends could be horse-shoed together with one hand.

With my other, I stroked her wet hair and caressed her face while she let out gasping screams until it was over, by which time my tears ran with hers and pooled on the metal surface beneath her. She had soiled herself in her distress. In mine, my throat had clenched through stifled lullabies and promises of getting her out of there. Somewhere between the second and third attempt at draining the spinal substance from her spine, Oliver protested repeatedly to the doctor, though he knew he was only doing his job.

When the lumbar puncture results also returned NAD (nothing abnormal discovered), I sensed the house doctor give up on his theory of septicemia, and Mathilda was transferred to a single room on the ENT unit. We were staying with her. Oliver shifted into a mental gear that drove him home and back within an hour, reappearing with a grocery bag clutched to his chest. The bag contained necessary baby supplies and toiletries, and a random selection of pre-maternity clothes, mostly winter wear that I wouldn't be able to match my girth for another year. By the time we had been moved to a single room, I was an emotional wreck, tearing up at the leads and machines she was already connected to. A night nurse came in, noted down the tachycardia then whisked back off to the desk to make a call. Since Mathilda's crying consistently jacked up the alarms sounding on her monitors, I attempted to draw her to me, angling her through the wires for a feed. It was difficult to block out the burning in my breasts and the distraction of her wheezing, but at some point I managed to latch her on, the various *beep-beeps* marking time and failing to bring the nurse back to us.

My anxiety over Mathilda's abnormal breathing held for another couple of hours, and by the time a female ENT registrar entered the room, I let her know all I was fearing of Mathilda's future. *What if I never get to show her the ocean, or take her to the farm and feed the lambs with her sister and brother? We have plans,* I said, *to walk through meadows, holding her hand and naming the butterflies that distract us from starting our picnic.* These were the hallmarks of a happy childhood that I could not reconcile with my baby, wired up to the hilt and drawing in breath as if she was sucking in water. After a brief examination, I went further, pressing the doctor for any reassurances she could offer me that would reset my equilibrium.

"You've just had a baby. You know, your emotions run wild at times like this. Try not to fret. It is important you get some rest," she said.

"You're right" I murmured. "But I need to know she's going to be okay." The part of me that could still process information picked out the relevant words of the doctor's response. *Tracheal tug, sternal recession-subcostal recession—possible laryngomalacia-endoscopy in the morning—Doctor Fitzwilliam, Pediatric Ear nose and throat consultant is very good—He is very good. She'll be fine.*

"What is laryngomalacia?" I asked.

"It's where the airways have not developed properly and the baby struggles to breathe. But they grow out of it eventually and in most cases without surgery." I was halfway through asking her the implications of the condition when her pager rang urgently with the sound of a crash call. The few pieces of information I had were reassuring enough for me to gather myself, hold Mathilda upright on my chest as she went on squeaking, and wait for the sun to climb through our window.

True to her word, the ENT registrar returned early with a small crew of ear, nose and throat specialists headed by Dr. Samuel Fitzwilliam. He struck me as I imagine he does most people, as a rather dashing, Dr. Kildare look-alike. His strong features and dangling dark curls around his temples were almost enough to distract a mother from relaying important information about her newborn's health. As I began to take in the jovial tone of the team's conversation, I felt myself relax whilst answering his questions about the last 24 hours, until I clapped eyes on the mobile endoscopy unit that was wheeled in and suddenly loomed large above my baby's head. Mathilda lay there, a six pound speck in the center of the room, unaware of the imminent procedure whilst the doctors began shuffling in around her. Between Fitzwilliam's thumb and index finger, a tiny camera at the end of a thick black wire snaked its way up into her nose and halted just above her larynx. On the black and white screen rigged up above us we all stared up at something that should not have been there. Like a deformed piece of piping.

"Ah, there it is." He let out proudly.

"What is it?" To me it looked like a curled up tongue. Piglet pink, with a white rim.

"There's the floppy ring of cartilage. The larynx has not matured."

"Is that what is making her sound squeaky?"

"Yep. Getting air past a floppy larynx means she is working hard to breathe."

"Is it treatable?" *Please say yes.*

"She'll grow out of it probably by her second birthday. We can give her some medication to settle the reflux in the meantime, which you'll need to administer before each feed. In the grand scheme of things it's a pretty minor condition. Nothing we can't handle."

"So we manage her breathing conservatively?" I asked, unsure of whether or not surgery was on the cards.

"We'll need to take a further look, but it can wait a week or two." Turning to a colleague Dr. Fitzwilliam asked for the surgery list to be checked and Mathilda to be placed on the schedule for a full bronchoscopy—this time under general anesthesia.

"Apart from that, is there any other treatment? She is

just going to carry on breathing like this for a couple more years?" I asked.

"She needs to be monitored, particularly her weight, but we can do that in clinic. We'll try and see her every couple of months or so to make sure she is maintaining her position on the growth chart and doing what she should be doing developmentally." He indulged my concerns further, largely about her feeding, and after explaining that her floppy larynx was just *one of those things* that can happen in utero, the mobile endoscopy unit was packed away. Once a date for the bronchoscopy was set, they all left.

If Dr. Samuel Fitzwiliam's easy-going manner had gone some way to encourage me, our discharge, conditional on Oliver and me passing resuscitation training, was enough to pull me back. Before we could take Mathilda home, we waited for a specialist nurse, who taught parents like us how to press life back into a baby using two fingers. Hoping neither one of us would ever have to employ her tricks on anything other than the dummy lying beside our real baby, we practiced over and over on the rubber torso, cocking back its stiff chin and sealing its nose and mouth with our lips. We counted each other's breaths in unison. *One and two and three and ...* taking turns to master the timing and the pressure we exerted on the dummy's sternum, pretending this was normal, something we could do. During that hour, I prayed we would never have to recall the details we were desperately trying to retain. What were the odds of us both being home and keeping this level of objectivity should her larynx cave in altogether? What if she stopped breathing at night and we didn't hear her? How would we stay sane with the constant rasping and potential reality of her choking?

The resuscitation nurse congratulated us before handing over a form and pen, "You've both passed, but I do need you to sign here. Just confirm that you'll be able to do this should anything happen," she said matter-of-factly, as we signed off with a confidence that belied our true feelings.

That last hour on the ENT unit left us unable to shake off any notion that Mathilda's breathing difficulties were without risk. We took our wheezing baby home and kept her within arms' reach, moving her with us around the house. Oliver and I discussed how best to position Mathilda during the night before finally acknowledging the fact that she would have to sleep with us, in our room, something we always said we would never do. Not least because he was a sound sleeper, and his 6 foot 3 inch, 225-pound frame could crush a baby. That aside, sharing a bed with your children could spell disaster for your marriage.

In the months that followed, there were daily episodes of choking, which we managed by holding her upright and waiting for her to draw back on air. Our goal was for Mathilda to put on weight so she would literally grow out of the condition, which meant pushing through with feeds even when they took an hour and were fraught with sudden rasping chokes. At night, her fight for breath frequently ended in silence, by which time one of us would bolt out of bed and pull her to a position in which she would gasp several times, then wheeze her way back to sleep.

Jennifer, the health visitor assigned to us by Dr. Bledsoe, visited weekly to monitor Mathilda's progress in a set of mobile weighing scales. Pulling the contraption from a large black bag, Mathilda's body was hooked up and dangled inside a square cloth that made her look as though she was about to be carried off by a pelican. Liberty and Elliot would sit on the lounge floor, wide-eyed every visit until their sister was released, their relief taking them back upstairs to their interrupted game.

"She's technically a failure to thrive," Jennifer said before tracking her weight on the lowest line of the growth chart.

"I am not too worried," I countered. "She just started to try and roll over and takes in everything going on around her." Physical milestones weren't a race in my mind, and catching up with a chart that I was beginning to resent was the very least of our worries.

"She just needs to put some weight on. But that will be slow because she is using all her calories to breathe. Keep up the feeding," she would say, before trailing off with armfuls of equipment towards the front door.

What mattered most in those months was that Mathilda never fully stopped breathing, and Oliver and I never needed to use our resuscitation training, though our own hearts stopped multiple times it seemed. In any given moment I swung from the panic of having to grab her and wait for a full inhale, to the pleasure of reading quietly to all three of them. When Mathilda had enough head control to be propped up in the bumbo seat, she watched Liberty and Elliot playing around her and absorbed everything they did, everything they said. If I was teaching them at the table, she sat with her head supported in the high chair, reaching for the pens or play dough on her tray to be part of the lesson, which she was. Very quickly Mathilda rewarded us by using her hands as signs for whatever she needed. With her tiny hands she let us know when she was hungry; they were squeezed into fists the way milk is drawn from an udder. Then she would say thank you by patting her chin. The baby sign for 'sorry' was a circle on her chest, and 'I love you' was both arms across her tiny torso until she verbalized the words we all wanted to hear.

Our lives gradually found a rhythm that enabled us to laugh, to learn and to look outside ourselves. In that sense, it was a very healthy experience. And although it was not the most straightforward start, Dr. Fitzwilliam was right— the limp larynx toughened up by her second birthday, by which time the harsh rasping sound of her breathing receded with each day, until it finally ceased altogether. That episode of her life and ours was over. Just like that.

5 PRINCETON
Late Summer 2008-Fall 2009

> "I like it better here. Where I can sit
> just quietly and smell the flowers."
>
> **—Munro Leaf**
> *The Story of Ferdinand*

Sometime in the New Year, Oliver rang me from work. He'd been waiting on an application made to spend the following year's research leave abroad, away from the office at Bristol. I picked up the phone and walked back into the garage where I was helping the kids with various art projects.

"Claire! Guess what?" His voice was urgent, excited.

"What? Go on." I had a hunch he had heard back from The Center of Theological Inquiry in Princeton.

"How do you fancy a year in New Jersey?"

"So you got it? That's so amazing. Congratulations. Of course I want to go!"

"It'll mean more upheaval but I think it'll be great. It's supposed to be beautiful there."

"I can't believe it. Tell them yes. Yes we'll come."

"Are you sure? We don't have to do this. I can work at

home for a year instead."

"Totally sure. What are you waiting for?"

We sold the idea of another year in America to the kids as our last big family adventure. With the ages of the children being 10, 8 and 2, this was quite likely the last time we would be able to travel in the way we had once done. Almost immediately we searched the internet for all the things we might do there: visit museums in DC, New York and Philadelphia. Nine months later, we rented out our house, and with a suitcase each, crossed the Atlantic to New York in September of 2009. The doors of the plane opened to a wall of heat, the air thick with freedom and anticipation. All five of us were wearing British clothes, unsuitable for the humidity in which we now found ourselves. Taking the Amtrak train from Liberty International Airport to Princeton Junction, we then hailed two cabs to our house on Ross Stevenson Circle, where a plate of cookies welcomed us on the porch, along with a yellow post-it that read, "Welcome to the Crisps!" provided by another academic family who had arrived two weeks earlier.

The faculty accommodation for visiting scholars consisted of large, blue clapboard houses that looped in a circle almost a mile round. Most of the homes were occupied by families that were temporary residents, as we were. Some were given to Princeton Seminary faculty—the few who had tenure status and lived on the Circle permanently.

What struck me most in the fifteen-minute drive from the train station to our new home were the trees. There were hundreds of them, great, green canopies arched across the roads, pregnant with birdsong and the vibrating cacophony of cicadas. I did not fall in love with Princeton's world-renowned university, the quadrangles or quaint streets, but with its scenery, seasons and opportunities. In our year there, we bought bikes for the kids from yard sales, which they rode freely round the Circle the way I had pedaled my red Raleigh in London in the '70s—without a care for cars or working brakes. In the fall we watched the trees turn the color of bonfires until the leaves dropped and disappeared under several feet of snow. The East Coast winter gave us skiing in Camelback, Pennsylvania, a two hour drive that Americans think nothing of, as well as endless hours of sledding on the Circle with other children home from school on "snow days." Spring came in gently by late March, displaying a beauty all of its own. The distinctness of each season, like something out of a children's book, left me speechless some days, following the river trail to the grocery store along roads that clung to the changing rhythms of each season. In all truth, I had never seen such raw beauty—the sort that makes everything right, and leaves you certain that something beyond yourself has ordered both time and place and made you fit so securely within it.

Well aware of being on borrowed time, I adapted our

own home-school routine to suit the children's needs and make the most of our new environment. For Libby and Elliot it meant a couple of days at an established learning center for home-educated children, where they took classes in Science, French and Art. I taught them Math, English, History and Geography the rest of the week, cramming necessary written work into the early mornings and leaving the rest of the day for play, reading and visits to the library. Several families in the Circle had started a preschool run in their homes on Monday and Thursday mornings. When Corrie Berg, another parent a few doors down, invited Mathilda to join the other three children in this co-operative endeavor, she gained a classroom in their lounge, and I gained the odd morning off once a fortnight when it was our turn to host the children. It was here that she made plenty of friends, mostly boys who were as mischievous and carefree as she was. The door bell rang day after day with other children who, like our own, were caught up in the moment of carefree play, oblivious to everything other than the immediacy of their games—catching fireflies in jars, larger than life butterflies or chasing the chipmunks that nested under our house. Mathilda, only two and fully restored from the failure to thrive she'd been labeled with, grew out of the developmental delays that had previously preoccupied us, and found her own voice. And all I did that year was watch.

Envelopes sealed with wax began arriving in our mailbox, and Oliver and I found ourselves at parties hosted by the President of the Seminary, Iain Torrance, who also happened to be Chaplain to the Queen and one of Oliver's former teachers at Aberdeen University. These events occasioned trivial conversations with scholars and dignitaries that we would probably never see again. I bought cocktail dresses from J. Crew, and we drove our pre-owned Honda Civic a mile to campus, leaving the children with baby sitters, another provision of the Circle. I quickly caught on that it would never do to stand too close to the chocolate fountains, fill up your bone china tea cup, double dip, or empty your champagne glass before you were offered another. There should always be some left swirling at the bottom of the glass. This was Ivy League life, where professional boundaries blurred with personal ones, and where you signaled that it was normal to have pictures of your family posing with royalty and ecclesiastical dignitaries along the mantelpiece.

Perhaps the times in Princeton that I remember most fondly were Fridays. By five in the evening, the adults on the Circle, done with the week's work, pulled their grills out to the large grass areas in front of our houses and joined the children, who were wheeling each other round Ross Stevenson Circle in Radio Flyer wagons. All I had to do was bring out our steak and salad and pool our wine, which we drank, along with beer, well beyond dusk and bedtime. It was so effortless, compared to the three square meals made in our pokey kitchen demanded by our lives back in the UK. We were part of an academic bubble, which was wonderful while it lasted, for in it we were safe. Nothing could get at us. Very likely, it was the first time the children had seen Oliver and me relax in a long while, laughing with friends and letting slide the kids' need to shower on occasion.

I would reflect on it years later, delving into those memories as one would pull out an old photo album to show a new friend. In retrospect, it doesn't seem real, that life could be so simple. When I turn back to that time, I see Elliot riding his bike, Liberty upside down turning cartwheels on the lawn, and Mathilda being chased by older kids until caught. She would go along with it, laughing before charging off, shouting for them to chase her again. And we had visitors, my parents, and my friend Wendy, who wondered out loud how we would ever adjust to life back home once the year was up. I half-heartedly answered her, but with my fingers firmly crossed behind my back. I actually hoped that we could stay, even though I knew the months were passing fast, and our flights home were already booked.

Counting down the weeks before returning home, I treasured our time there whilst willing the days to slow, until we could hold onto them no longer. Posting on Facebook that our days in paradise were well and truly over, we exchanged painful good-byes with our friends on the Circle. We finally took ourselves and our same luggage back home to England via a two-week summer school job in Vancouver—a stretch of time that, under different circumstances, would have been met with great appreciation on our part. Instead, Oliver and I found ourselves fighting both flu and depression as the final moments toward returning home became an inescapable reality.

It was July of 2009 when we descended through the low turbulent clouds of Bristol. I would have to draw on my own resources to pick up our lives in a place that couldn't have been more different from the one we had left. On our journey back, Oliver and I talked about the order in which we needed to do things, such as organizing the house, returning to work and starting home-school again. We asked the children what they were looking forward to—meeting their new cousin, (my sister's newborn), bringing down all their toys from the attic, being in their own beds, or the Saturday sweet shop at the end of our street. They always took their cues from us, so we talked it up, saying things about Bristol we didn't really believe ourselves. I turned to the window as the wheels abruptly screeched along the tarmac and cried a little. Beyond the downpour and blur of the airport was the burden of us all readjusting, and it weighed on me like a rope of stones around my neck. I was prepared for the challenges of raising our kids again. Yet, to this day, if I had had any idea of what was ahead, I would never have boarded that plane.

6 BATCH NO. A81CA149A
January 16, 2010

> "I felt a sharp pain in my hip; then it was over. What they were injecting and why, I did not know, yet for twenty of us those injections were to change our whole lives."
>
> —**Robert C. O'Brien**
> ***Mrs Frisby and the Rats of Nimh***

It was anticipated that the swine flu virus of 2009 would tip pandemic scales and claim the lives of hundreds of thousands of people worldwide as it had done throughout the previous century. Fearing a repeat of the Spanish Flu of 1918 where H1N1 thrived in the trenches and killed more soldiers than on the battlefields (with estimates ranging from eight to fifty million deaths total), the World Health Organization (WHO) officially declared the existing H1N1 infection a global pandemic. Within weeks, European governments responded by contracting with major multinational pharmaceutical companies, including GlaxoSmithKline (GSK), to formulate an effective vaccine. A prototype was developed, resulting in the vaccine, Pandemrix. By December 2009, we received a letter from our local doctor requesting that Mathilda be brought in for the free vaccination program on January 16. Every other family in the UK with a child under five years of age also received such a request. The WHO, together with governments across the globe, supported scientific concerns that this H1N1 virus would target the young and medically vulnerable, potentially resulting in serious complications and high rates of admissions to critical care units.

Our letter also stated that Pandemrix was a "safe and effective licensed vaccine approved by the European Commission" and would result in "non-serious complications, which were in line with expectations." What the letter did not mention, however, was that the vaccine Pandemrix had not been tested or authorized on children. Parents like us were unaware of this crucial detail, a fact that I have since tried very hard to come to terms with. Moreover, the vaccine was "adjuvanted" and contained not only the H1N1 antigen but also a chemical compound called Squalene. Adjuvants are advantageous since they intensify the effectiveness of a vaccine by turbo-boosting the body's immune system, resulting in a "hyper-activation." "They are used to elicit an early, high, and long-lasting immune response," according to the Vaccine Risk Awareness Network. From a pharmacological point of view, the fact that Pandemrix elicited a very strong immune response meant efficacy was high.

The antigen itself was in short supply in 2009 and 2010, resulting in the production of a vaccine in which a minimal amount of antigen was used to attain the required response—a process known as "antigen sparing." Using an adjuvanted vaccine further increased supply by as much as fourfold, and consequently, greater numbers of people could receive the vaccine before H1N1's sweep through the country.

In a climate of socialized healthcare where the government foots the bill with taxpayers' money, a more affordable and timely vaccine for a large proportion of the population was then a very attractive option. Later, debate about the use of Squalene and the strength of the vaccine given to young children that year would preoccupy scientists and doctors. They had rarely seen young children present in their offices with symptoms of narcolepsy—a profoundly disabling neurological condition. The original vaccine called for two doses, one shot followed by another several weeks later. Soon it was obvious that the immune response was so robust that by the time the vaccine was given out to the UK, only one jab was required.

What was the link between the H1N1 vaccine and the surge in numbers of these children? Some researchers believe it was the H1N1 virus itself that was involved, devastating the immune system, which fought the virus as it was supposed to, but also killed the hypocretin cells in the hypothalamus—the loss of which resulted in narcolepsy. Others think the vaccine was just too strong while some maintain the adjuvant theory. To date, the precise mechanism that triggered the destruction of hypocretin cells is still being debated. Yet, no doubt is cast over the reality: the 2010 H1N1 vaccine brought about hundreds of cases of narcolepsy in both children and adults.

At the same time, as more cases emerged in Europe, it became evident that some children were developing symptoms of the devastating sleep disorder although they had received a different vaccine—one without an adjuvant. Different children had merely been exposed to the flu from family members, and others had no knowledge or recollection of either exposure or the vaccine.

In our opinion, Mathilda had already spent enough time in the company of doctors at Bristol Children's Hospital. Although she had outgrown her laryngomalacia, reflux and failure to thrive, she was still slight for her age and had only turned the corner in the past year. None of us had ever had a flu shot before. Because of Mathilda's potential vulnerability and the anticipated impact of the H1N1 virus on children her age, Oliver and I thought this might be the one time we should consider a flu vaccine for one of our kids. Having discussed this at home, together, we made the decision to go ahead. In reality, it was I who drove her there.

It happened on Saturday, January 16, 2010. I ploughed through a rainstorm with the window wipers going full blast, driving through the water-logged streets to our newly remodeled family health center. All three children were huddled in the back, and we talked of what they might do indoors that day once we returned home. We found the waiting room teeming with rambunctious toddlers and parents waiting their turn. They had come solely for the same reason we had—the vaccine. I was struck by the scale of it all. The children sat on the floor beside me as I handed them each a book to try to read through the chaos.

"Crisp, Mathilda?" One of the doctors, a spritely young woman, eventually called us in from the large doors that separated the seating area from the rest of the health center.

"Yes! That's us, kids. Let's go." I sprang up, stuffed our things into my bag and grabbed Mathilda's hand. Anxious not to lose the doctor as she bounced down the long corridor at a pace closer to a light jog than a walk, I urged Elliot and Liberty to hurry. The health center had turned the large front office into a makeshift clinic. All the over-sized desks, top heavy with phones and files, were pressed to the walls while temporary vaccinating stations were erected in their place. With her typical jolliness, Dr. Larsen motioned for us to sit in one of the large black office chairs in the corner. As Mathilda climbed up on my lap, I fixed my feet firmly on the floor to avoid the two of us twirling round when the needle went in.

"You have a busy day ahead," I commented, now facing a large circle of other parents trying to keep siblings from wheeling the chairs around the room. The already vaccinated children were crying. Others were trying to physically avoid the needle poised before them. Usually we saw a doctor within the privacy of a single medical room. This morning's clinic resembled some bizarre mass-herding project. A burly nurse in every-day clothes approached us, and without introducing herself, picked up the vaccine on the mobile tray unit and double-checked the batch number in unison with the doctor. Together they intoned, "H1N1, A81CA149A, Right arm, expiry August, 10."

"This is just a little scratch and is very quick," Dr. Larsen said encouragingly over the rising levels of distress.

"You'll be fine Mathilda. Look at me sweetheart," I said, pulling her in tight and turning away from the tray of needles and band-aids.

"Can you hold her arm still? You're such a brave little girl." Dr. Larsen drew up the syringe of Pandemrix and prepared the cotton ball and records. I motioned for Libby to pull the lid off the treat box we had brought as a distraction should Mathilda cry as the needle went in. Inside was a packet of Cadbury's chocolate buttons. Saturdays were candy days in our house, and most weeks, with 50 pence in their pockets, the children walked down to the corner shop and picked out a treat. On this occasion, I had brought the sweets with us.

Elliot was looking nervous. "What's the injection for? Do I have to come back for one?" He was staring at the ring of children across the office.

"This is just for little kids, and we give it to them to protect them from getting really sick." Dr. Larsen was speaking whilst finishing up with Mathilda's arm that I was still gripping tightly.

"Tonight you should give her Calpol [Tylenol] in case she has a fever. Otherwise, you are all done. What a good girl. You were so brave," she said, wiping the blood and applying pressure to the small mark below her shoulder. I rubbed the circular band-aid in place, took Mathilda off my lap and whispered to Elliot that it was rude to stare at the other children who were about to be subjected to the same shot in either one of their arms.

It took three seconds for Mathilda to receive the H1N1 vaccine that was supposed to prevent serious illness. Just a moment for 24% of British parents to unknowingly subject their children to a vaccine that had only been tested on a small portion of adults; even these clinical trials had not been completed to an adequate level of safety. Across Europe, 37% of children between the ages of 2 and 15 were similarly vaccinated with Pandemrix by March of 2010.

Sweden and Finland were the first countries to alert the rest of the world to the unprecedented rise in childhood narcolepsy, a serious and incurable autoimmune illness rarely seen below the age of fifteen. Only after did this same realization hit Britain. As around 1,500 children across Europe became neurologically sick, what emerged over the following months was the possibility that the H1N1 vaccine had backfired. For the British government and GSK, it was another pharmacological headache. For hundreds of children and families, it became a personal tragedy.

The weather took a darker turn as the four of us left the health center and headed home. I called Oliver to hold off on the lunch he was preparing since the appointment went much quicker than I expected. I looked up at Mathilda in the rear-view mirror and praised her for not crying when she had the injection. Passing the box of candy back to where all three were laughing, the four of us drove back towards home, and an uneventful weekend.

And that was it. How easy it was to unknowingly flip all our lives over in one short ride. Since then I have gone back to what should have been an unremarkable hour, grappling with guilt and painful regret through endless nights of sleep deprivation and days of watching Mathilda sleep her childhood away. All the symptoms of narcolepsy and suffering crystallized in the seconds it took for her to have the H1N1 vaccine. Many times I have imagined myself ripping the kitchen clock off the wall and turning back the hands of time, taking her to the candy store, the park, anywhere but to the clinic that would ruin her life. I wish she had cried, protested, screamed and refused the needle. I wished she had begged me to take her home. But she was three years old. She trusted me, and I in turn foolishly trusted in a system that was supposed to keep her safe.

We don't talk about it often. The last time Mathilda asked me why she can't sleep like other kids was several years ago. We were in the bathroom drawing up her nighttime medication and preparing a small tray of food that would stop her from vomiting in the morning. I explained how she was one of hundreds of children to develop narcolepsy as a result of the swine flu vaccine.

"Did it hurt me when the needle went in?" she asked.

"Not at the time. You didn't even flinch."

"So if it didn't hurt, why did I get narcolepsy?"

"It doesn't work like that darling. Just because the vaccine didn't hurt you on the outside, doesn't mean it didn't damage you on the inside."

"Did you want me to have the vaccine?" She said starting to brush her teeth.

"Yes and no. I didn't want you to get sick with the flu.

But if I'd have known you would get narcolepsy, I wouldn't have taken you that day. It's hard being a Mom sometimes, because we always want the best for our children but we can't always control what happens. And that means difficult things come along, things that we want to take away but we can't."

"I like it when you say you wish you could take away my narcolepsy, but I don't want *you* to have it."

"That's kind. It's true sweetheart, if I could take it away, I would." I set the timer on the safe that would protect her from taking the second dose before 3 a.m. Mathilda rinsed out her mouth, and before wiping her face dry, looked at me and said:

"I'm tired."

'It's okay. Let's get to bed. Dad is on first dose. Do you want to go say goodnight to him?"

"I'm too sleepy. Can he come in to me?"

"Of course."

We walked just a few feet to Mathilda's bed. I lifted the two cats off the pillows and turned them out for the night through the farmhouse door in her room. As I covered her with a Disney-style blanket and removed books, pens and various scribbled notes strewn across the bed, she rolled towards the wall. Drowsy, and a few moments away from another night of fractured sleep and medication, Mathilda lifted her hand and reached for me. I took her slender fingers and placed Cocoa, her love-worn bear, under her arm. Even now, her final words still resonate, as if to absolve me from a day and a decision that would leave her brain-damaged.

"You're a great mom for me."

"And you are my favorite seven-year-old in the whole world."

"Can you rub my feet? They hurt."

"Sure. Where's the pain?" Oliver appeared in the doorway to say goodnight and saw me rubbing Mathilda's ankles. I thought by then she was already gone—succumbing to the inevitable hallucinations that would torment her for the next several hours. Oliver began clearing the floor from the bed to the doorway, picking up American Girl doll accessories and other soft toys, more books and a wet towel. Turning off the nightstand, I walked towards the hallway and heard a final faint murmur—words that would do much to connect us but little to assuage my remorse.

"Mom, you did what you thought was best for me," she whispered.

7 GOOD FRIDAY, BAD FRIDAY
Easter 2010

"It has been a terrible, horrible, no good, very bad day. My Mom says some days are like that."

—Judith Vorst
Alexander and the Terrible, Horrible, No Good, Very Bad Day

The first few weeks after the vaccination Mathilda started having vivid dreams at night. We thought little of it at the time. She had, after all, begun reading since our return from Princeton, picking up children's books around the house, decoding words and phonetically making sense of every story line. If she didn't quite get a sentence, she would move on, aided by the illustrations and a firm literary narrative that played out in her head. I wondered if she was simply re-living these tales at night. This new crying out, thrashing around and abrupt exiting out of sleep was strange, but we had another reason for thinking Mathilda's recent wakings were within the bounds of normality. She was highly imaginative. Ayah, her four-inch make-believe friend, lived permanently on her right shoulder back then. They went everywhere together. In the car, the two of them engaged themselves in tireless conversations that were difficult to interrupt; it was almost impossible to get a word in edgeways. Sometimes Mathilda swiped her off her shoulder and carried her around on her index finger, the way you would a parrot. Ayah then carried on the conversation once the two of them were eye-level, even when there were other children to play with. It was something to watch, and I let myself believe Ayah was merely invading her dream world too.

By the end of February, Oliver and I were waking up with Mathilda half a dozen times a night, every night. Nearly always this was because she was crying through a dream that she could not shake off, sometimes because she had fallen out of bed, or banged her head against the wall, as if trying to escape something, we didn't know what.

Around this time, she also began to struggle with Pre-K, although not initially. Our local primary school, just a mile from our house, had a classroom attached to it for three-year-olds, and I signed her up so I could spend time alone with the older two. Elliot had showed signs of depression since coming back from Princeton, something I had never seen in a child before. He was tearful, unmotivated and emotionally hard to reach. After finding him curled up and hiding under his bunk bed rather than playing, crying before bedtime, and snapping pencils in half during school work, I decided to spend several afternoons a week just with him and Liberty. We used the time Mathilda was in Pre-K to visit museums and libraries, to take long nature walks, and on very wet days, to go to Ikea for meatballs. When I asked him how he was feeling about being back in Bristol, his seven-year-old response told me what I already knew.

"Mum, the doorbell never rings for me anymore."

"But you do have a lot of friends here Els. And you see them almost every day," I reasoned, hoping to instill in him the positive sides of being home.

"I know Mum," he said. "But it's not the same."

He missed everything about the year we lived in the US. The people, the place and strong sense of community. We all did. But there was no going back, and as I saw it, my job was to help him in particular to move on.

The fall of 2009 came and went quickly that year, giving up its colors to harsh winds and early morning frosts that held through to the afternoons. At the end of Mathilda's first term, I met with her teacher, Maggie, a tall willowy woman in her forties who had worked with preschoolers for twenty or so years. She had no need for make-up, and her loose brown waves of hair hung as low as the pockets of her linen smock. When it was time to leave for home, almost all of the children hugged her goodbye. One or two refused to let go of her legs until she pried their arms from her thighs with promises of seeing them the next day. A week before Christmas, we sat in a small room just off the main classroom. We reviewed graphs of Mathilda's progress in a large booklet. Every page had some sort of complex flow diagram that was hard to track unless your three-year-old had mastered the academic, physical and social skills demanded by the National Curriculum. A green track indicated good work; amber, so-so; and red, not so good. After an hour or so of charting Mathilda's progress with a green marker, I had only one question.

"When Mathilda is here, is she happy?"

"Yes, very," Maggie replied. "She is a natural leader. I pair her up with children for whom English is a second language, she helps them change for PE, and is the first to clear up when I ring the bell." She went on about how inventive she was during free play, how verbal during circle time, and independent at self-care. I felt that the meeting was a waste of both of our time, a ridiculous jumping through hoops enforced by the National Curriculum, and not necessarily helpful to children like Mathilda. I had the upmost respect for Maggie. She was that rare individual who could balance calm with authority, adding a sprinkling of love. No wonder the children were drawn to her like a magnet.

But three weeks into the night terrors, and a month post the vaccine, our next conversation took a different turn. The several afternoons Mathilda went to Pre-K became physically demanding for her, and by the time we walked a hundred feet to the car at pick up, she was miserable and needed to be carried. I was concerned about how Mathilda was falling apart as she came out of the classroom. But then again, I had also become frustrated with the deterioration in her behavior, which I reasoned went hand in hand with the tiredness. I sat down late into a cold Friday afternoon to take the weight off my feet and called the school. The woman running the front desk had Maggie ring me back.

"Mathilda has recently started waking up a lot at night, with terrible nightmares, and is having trouble getting from the school gate to the car in one piece," I said. "She cries all the way home. Have you noticed anything different about her?"

"I have. I was going to speak to you about it," said the voice at the other end of the phone. "She's not been her bonny self these past few weeks and seems lethargic, easily upset. The bruise on her head, is that related?" She asked.

Teachers in England go through extensive training to identify signs of child abuse. I was suddenly on the spot, but I was also concerned that her falling apart had something to do with her being there—that for some reason she now hated it.

"A few nights ago, she thrashed across the bed and hit her head on the wall. I am sure she was acting out her nightmare." There was a long pause. I felt I needed to explain it further, but I had nothing besides the broken sleep, and I was still convinced it was a problem related to external factors. Nothing more. The only thing I was certain of was that Mathilda was not coping with being out of the house for four hours a week. I needed to give her a break from being there.

"Claire," she said. "Mathilda is trying to tell you something. You need to do what you think is best." I felt grateful for her experience with young children and her agreeing to give us a few weeks off, in spite of the fact it was midterm. For whatever reason, her time with Maggie and the other children wasn't working.

"As soon as she's through this phase," I replied, "I'll let you know and bring her back in."

I hung up with the reassurance they would hold her place open until she was ready to return, which I honestly thought wouldn't be more than couple of weeks.

Our home school routine was in full throttle, and I began to plan on projects the three children could do together. Apart from their obsession with building fairy houses, we also dug a small but successful pond in the back garden behind one of the flowerbeds. Lined with black plastic, the tiny waterhole was not complete without plants and a few hundred tadpoles. We collected this in old jam jars from a much larger pool of water in a wooded area on the southwest corner of the city. Over several weeks, the children watched the tiny, black frogspawn until they turned into real frogs. Only four made it, but that was enough for us to witness life cycles, understand food chains and watch the frogs return the following spring. Liberty saw them as pets and named each of them. There was something about the natural rhythm of such home days that were centering and purposeful. Yet looking back, they distracted me from spotting signs of something far more serious.

There was also the two days a week shared teaching with Wendy and Mary, good friends of mine who also home-educated their children. Wendy and I took it in turns to lead the lessons for each day. With the five older children we linked history with art and geography and served a hot lunch from whatever country we were studying. Our chemistry lessons included creating molecules from marshmallows and toothpicks utilizing a hands-on curriculum that explained advanced concepts in simple ways. The preparation for these co-op days was intense but the children loved learning together and there was never a time when I felt we hadn't achieved something unique because our little kitchen was filled with laughter and years later all the children could recall what they had studied. And because of the way Wendy and I designed the schedule, one day every three weeks each adult gained a day off.

In turn, Mathilda and Emily had a daylong play date with Mary's youngest, Evie. Looking after the little ones was mostly Mary's concern—she had an effortless calm when it came to being with young children for hours. Our co-op two days a week continued, but Mathilda's difficult behavior was now something I felt I needed to address with more focus. Sending her off for a time out every time she was disobedient wasn't working and I was at a loss on how best to handle her new temper tantrums.

"If she is getting away with stuff at night, Claire, she'll get away with it in the day," Wendy offered one day at pick-up.

"Honestly, it's as if she is having the 'terrible twos' all over again. I can't get a handle on what is making her defiant and miserable or how to turn it round," I said.

Confiding that I was struggling was as good as admitting I was useless at basic parenting, even after three children. I also knew that when I was floundering, failing even, Wendy would offer support without judgment. She offered a final suggestion before leaving my place with bags of books and her four impeccable offspring.

"You can do this Claire. You just need to make it a priority."

It took a conversation like that to make me semi-charged with a renewed determination for getting Mathilda back on the straight and narrow. And although I was already feeling the ill effects of physical exhaustion, I was resolute in thinking she was just acting up. I could handle a disobedient child with my eyes shut but the only way I could really give Mathilda the full attention she needed was to stay back from social events, the way you would if you were potty training your toddler. I was optimistic that a few weeks of intentional parenting, even if it meant being housebound, would be enough to bring Mathilda back.

One night that spring, not long after we had been recording the growth of our thriving tadpoles, Mathilda let out a piercing shriek that was not in any way typical. I flew into her room, where she was panicking and thrashing around the bed. I scooped her up.

"Hey, hey, Mummy's here. What's the matter?" Oliver, behind me, snapped on the light.

"Get it away! He's on me." She was screaming and sweating all at once. "Mummy. Help me!"

I pulled her in close to me and began rocking, my arms tight around her body.

"What is frightening you?" I asked.

"The frog. It's on me. Get it off!"

"There's no frog darling. They're in the garden. You're safe. It's just a dream. A bad dream."

"I can feel it. He's on me. He's here and he's big and bouncing on my tummy! Get him off! Get him off me!" She pushed the air with her hands as if to escape the weight of it, her eyes wide open. It was hard to say if she was awake or still dreaming. I tried to pull her out of it by carrying her downstairs although I did not know what I would do when I got there. In the kitchen I set her down on the counter, hoping the chill surface on the back of her legs would bring her back to her senses. Oliver boiled the kettle for a pot of tea whist I brushed Mathilda's wet hair from her face. We began talking about other, mundane things; this began to calm her a little.

"The frog was in my room, Daddy. He touched me. I don't want to go back there."

"There's no frog darling," Oliver said. "You've had a bad dream. That's all."

"He is real," she said. "He's frightened Ayah away."

"When we go back upstairs, we will check and make sure he's gone. And we'll look for Ayah. She's not far away," he said.

For the better part of an hour, we sat and talked around our oak table that occupied half the kitchen, with Mathilda on my lap while I rolled back and forth in the rocking chair. Once she was relaxed enough to go back to bed, we settled her in with a song and a prayer. We left the hall light on. Oliver was awake enough to give up on sleeping and start work. Thirty minutes later her dreaming started all over again, and I too gave up on getting any sleep.

§

On Good Friday, the five of us went to a service at Redland Church before heading to London for a family reunion. An imposing Georgian building, the church rested on an expanse of green land overlooking the sprawling city sprinkled with tower blocks. We walked through the iron gates that morning, passing thousands of daffodils turning their yellow heads our way with the wind. Once inside, we filed into a pew halfway down on the left. The somber mood was reflected in the cold stone memorial tablets flanking the inside walls. Each inscription testified to a life that at one time had been purposeful, cut short by war perhaps, but each one recognized for the meaningful contribution and subsequent loss. I liked that it was quiet and calm. The atmosphere was conducive to a re-centering whereby I could sit down in silence and empty my head, even if it was only for a few short moments before the service began.

Then, as we stood to greet people, Mathilda reached her hands and gestured to be lifted. When I sat down, she fell asleep, breathing deep against my body. It didn't particularly bother me that it was ten in the morning, or that the lady sitting next to me, a retired family physician, kept staring. But then, after the service, Mathilda slept through the two-hour drive along the M4 corridor to my Aunt Chris's bungalow. On arriving at the family party, she stayed asleep.

"I think we need to put her down, Chris. Is that okay?" I asked, walking over the threshold and directly to her bedroom at the front of the house. With a little more sleep, I expected that she would bound through the lounge, refreshed and ready to join her second cousins, running rings around adults as they lifted their glasses over the children's heads. The party, already in full swing, was in part to celebrate the arrival of my uncle Fred visiting from California. He had never met Mathilda, and I was eager for her to wake up and join in. When I checked on her an hour later, she was still knocked out, oblivious to the swell of voices inside and rush of traffic on the main road. Oliver suggested we take her home, and my mother, equally concerned, came into the bedroom. No one had yet seen Mathilda, and Mum wanted to be the one to introduce her to Fred, her brother. She was intensely proud of her grandchildren, delighting in their presence when the wider family gathered on rare occasions like this. The three of us stood over the bed and reasoned she might be coming down with something, perhaps a fever or a cold.

"Tilly. It's Nanny. Time to wake up." Mathilda stirred, pushed my Mum away then turned her back on us. She continued sleeping but my Mum went on, "I'll carry you if you are tired. Aunty Chris has a treat for you. Let's go and see where she is. Come on now, Nanny is here." Mum said before reaching down, lifting Mathilda's tiny frame into her own. Gently they walked into the garden through the crowded lounge all the while explaining that she has just woken up and would be up for greeting in just a few moments.

I finished my drink in the kitchen and watched Chris and Mum through the patio door. They passed Mathilda from one pair of arms to the others, offering her lollipops that the other children already had. Both of them persisted in comforting her, stroking her hair and face, but Mathilda pushed them away pumping her legs in protest. She was implacable. Oliver shot me a look that said 'we need to go,' his sense of embarrassment transparent and strong enough to make a sharp exit. We left grabbing our bags, and trailed in his route march to the car, Mathilda crying on his hip. Buckling her into the back, he reprimanded her for being rude and ungrateful, while I loaded the other two in.

"Mum, why are we leaving so early?" Elliot inquired as I bent over him checking his seatbelt.

"Mathilda's not feeling well. We need to get her home so she can rest."

"Why, what's wrong with her? I wanted to stay later," Libby said.

"I don't know," I replied. "But I'm sure it's nothing serious."

That Easter weekend, I expected Mathilda to spike a fever or come down with a virus, though she never did. Instead, she simply slept the days away, waking only to fuss and find fault with the world. I don't know where she went on the long drawn out nights that followed, or if we ever really reached her as we leapt from our bed to hold and comfort her. The delight she took in books and playing diminished, and she never fully recovered to return to Maggie at Pre-K. It would be another two years until she would meet her great-uncle Fred. When she did, it was not in England, but in California.

Worse than any of that, Ayah had left her.

8 COLLAPSE
April 12th 2010

> "There is nothing sweeter than the sound
> of someone calling your name."
>
> **—Kate DiCamillo**
> *The Tale of Despereaux*

Mathilda's appointment with our family physician was scheduled for after our return from a few days stay at my parents' house. Whilst Oliver took the train up to Manchester for a conference, I headed to the South Coast where my mum and dad lived, just a two-minute walk from Mudeford beach. Even more idyllic was their blue beach hut lined up in a row with other huts in postcard formation along the iconic shoreline, facing the Isle of Wight, and beyond that, France. Inside, the smell of creosote mixed with salt lingered on wetsuits, bunting, and a small collection of lighthouse ornaments. It was a place we loved, a glorified six-by-seven-foot shed that we unlocked on every visit and that stored treasured memories blanketed in sand.

Now harboring a deep concern for her daytime sleepiness, I had spent the first night lying next to Mathilda, trying to keep her nocturnal movements and moaning from disturbing the rest of the household. Early the next morning I met my parents in the kitchen where Dad was making coffee. Mum turned from the sink with her usual gentleness.

"Claire, Mathilda was awake most of the night wasn't she?"

"I'm sorry. I tried to keep her quiet. You didn't get much sleep, then?" I asked.

"No. But then, neither did you, love. We don't have to go out today if you would rather stay back, or I can take Libs and Els down to the beach and you can join us later."

"Well, she's asleep now so, yeah, maybe that would be best." I replied, impressed that Mum was able to rally, despite a broken night.

"I'll stay back with you both," Dad offered, sensing my anxiety.

"Seems so strange, her waking and calling out all the time," he said. "What do you think is wrong with her?"

"I have no idea, but I have her booked for a doctor's appointment on Wednesday, soon as we get back. I want her looked at."

Mostly I wanted Mathilda to charge down the stairs and declare her readiness to join the children frolicking on the front lawn as we organized towels and swimsuits. She would be indignant at the idea of being left behind, on missing out. But deep down I knew that wouldn't happen, and within minutes of the older two skipping off to the beach, a bucket in each hand, she called to me from the top of the stairs where she was perched. I was aware of Dad organizing photos on his computer in the lounge as I looked up at Mathilda. She seemed far away.

"We've missed you Mimi. Are you hungry for breakfast?" It was true. I was beginning to miss this little girl, despite spending the night with her. My constant companion looked pale and disheveled, and by then, had begun to withdraw deep into herself.

"Where is everyone Mumma?" she asked, her voice quiet and shaky. "Nanny took Libby and Elliot out, but Grey-Grey is here," I replied. "Are you ready for breakfast?"

I watched her bump down each step slowly on her backside, wearing PJs that were covered in blue Easter bunnies. By the time I reached the kitchen, she had followed me to the doorway, looking through me with hooded eyes as I stood on the other side of the room. The part of me that was troubled by her decline wanted to observe her walking. I bent low, tilted my head and reached my arms out, beckoning her to move toward me. There was something new, a remoteness about her that switched on an objective set of tools I had as a clinician. I assessed Mathilda the way I might have perhaps assessed a neurological patient years back.

"Come, sweet girl," I said gently. "Let's see what there is to eat."

I can summon the moment she swayed toward me in a heartbeat. The sandy, stone floor tiles, the running tap and the sun radiating from the window behind, illuminating her where she stood. She took three slow steps with her arms outstretched, then faintly uttered, "Mu-um-Ma." She steadied herself, locking her knees as if to stave off what was coming, before folding in half at the waist to the floor, then half again until she was down. I saw her white socks, her arm, twisted outwards and her face covered by her long matted hair. How the silence chilled the room and fell across my whole world, until I broke it with the cry of her name.

In the second it took me to reach her, a thousand questions flooded my mind. I tried to process what might be wrong; I rationalized my thoughts before succumbing to panic. Dad was there, kneeling with me. We called to her, willing a response, whilst I wiped the hair off her face so she could hear us. "Tilda! Tilda! What's Wrong? Tilda! Talk to me. It's Mummy. Can you hear me sweetheart?" Say something!"

Was she breathing? Yes
Did she have a pulse? Yes
Was she having a seizure? No
Was she responsive? No
Was she conscious? Dad panicked.

I don't know. I can't tell. I don't know. I don't know!

Bournemouth Hospital should have been a twenty-minute drive as the crow flies. Dad did his best to weave through the center of town in midday traffic, but the roads were congested, on purpose, it felt. Mathilda was cradled in my arms, and the seatbelt stretched wide around us in the back seat. I swung from parental terror to the ridiculously banal. I noticed all the reasons I disliked the place, now more than ever. We crawled past endless red-bricked houses, oil-marked driveways, and dated and dilapidated community buildings. Our world was falling apart. Lost on other drivers trundling blindly in the wrong lane, a centrifugal force pulled us to Accident and Emergency, I should have called an ambulance.

One thing the National Health Service does well is provide large waiting rooms. Despite being assessed by a triage nurse shortly after our arrival, Dad and I sat holding Mathilda for the better part of the next five hours. I called Oliver, explaining that we were at Bournemouth Hospital, that Mathilda had collapsed and that we couldn't rouse her. He decided to leave the conference he had organized early and meet us back in Bristol the next day. I would let him know as soon as there was news. Dad, in turn, left the waiting room for a few minutes to make a similar phone call to my mum. Apart from me handing the phone over to him, there was almost no exchange between us.

At one point, possibly three hours in, dad walked to the vending machine, returning with two stale sandwiches and a juice box for Mathilda. But if the loud group of laughing teenagers next to us, one with a sprained ankle, couldn't rouse her, I doubted a carton of apple juice would either. I grew frustrated with what seemed like minor ailments, coughs, rashes, and the like, walking past us, to the point where I approached the reception desk, not for the first time, holding Mathilda limp in my arms.

"Please. My daughter needs to be seen urgently. She collapsed several hours ago and hasn't been able to walk since. I can't wake her up." I put the shame of sounding desperate behind our critical need to see a doctor not caring what the triage nurse had documented, or what any of the staff thought of my request.

"She's been triaged?"

"Yes. And I don't understand why non-urgent cases are being taken in before we are. There is something seriously wrong with her."

"If the only problem is that she is asleep, then I am sure the nurse will call you when they are ready. We have your details," she said curtly.

"It's *not* the only problem." I replied. "She's been unable to sleep properly at night for weeks, and she can't stay awake during the day." The woman carried on typing, making no effort to look up.

"She just sounds very tired to me," she said. Like it was nothing.

"I am a physical therapist." I told her, pulling out anything that might add weight to our situation, for it seemed that being a mother was not enough.

"I'm certain something serious is wrong with her," I repeated.

"As I said," the receptionist replied, "you will be called in due course. Take a seat. Your turn will come."

I wanted to say more—that I was losing my daughter, had been for weeks, that a deep-seated realization that Mathilda was neurologically sick was gripping me, that there was no going back—but it was pointless.

Hours later we were ushered behind a curtain in the ER room. A young apologetic doctor re-took her vitals and reviewed her medical history before issuing me a small orange specimen pot. As if Mathilda knew that now was the time to wake up, slowly she roused herself from her slumber. I carried her to the bathroom and held her over the toilet, trying to squeeze a urine sample out of her, but she kept saying there was no more. I wanted to cry.

"Just try and wee honey. Then we can be done," I pleaded.

"I can't Mumma. There's no wee in me," she slurred.

"We only need a little. I know you can do it." I tried to sound upbeat.

It took further coaxing, then bargaining, to persuade her to sip the apple juice through a straw that I held to her mouth while my other hand was underneath her, anticipating each drop or small surge in flow. When I narrowly missed the aim and felt the hot fluid spreading across my hand, I swore, something I tried not to do in front of the children. Eventually, she must have produced enough urine. Years later, on scanning her medical notes, I read that her urine sample showed a raised white blood count, which may have explained the doctor's diagnosis that day of a urinary tract infection. But he also said she might have sleep apnea, though nothing was made of that. We left with a prescription for antibiotics and a letter to our family doctor, who was advised to follow up with an Ear, Nose and Throat referral in Bristol. Part of me was glad to leave with something as simple as a pink bottle of Trimepthoprim, but neither Dad nor I could shake off what we had seen that morning, what we instinctively knew was something sinister.

By evening time, Mum had made fish pie, Liberty's favorite supper, and opened a bottle of wine—regardless of the fact it was a Monday. My parents usually reserved alcohol for weekends and special celebrations, but in the unspoken fear of what we could neither understand nor deny, the three of us ate and drank blindly, our conversation preoccupied with the older kids' time in the ocean—a fleeting relief of normality.

Lacking the will or wherewithal to get back to an empty house immediately, I decided to stay one more night, risking driving on a couple of broken hours of sleep in the morning. I also needed the support of my parents, even though there was little they could do. Something about our situation stirred within me a desperate desire to retreat to a place of safety, where someone would remove my sense of foreboding. With Liberty and Elliot entertained in the lounge, and Mathilda asleep on the sofa, my parents watching her, I walked into the hallway. The past few weeks, and weight of that day, had knocked me down to a joyless spot on the stairs, leaning against the banister with last of the red wine in one hand and the phone in the other. There I sat talking to Oliver, letting the alcohol reach me in a way his reassurances couldn't.

The next day, I took Mathilda to see Dr. Hussain, one of the partners at Fishponds Family Practice in Bristol. It was late in the afternoon, and a sharp wind blew across the parking lot, flinging my door wide as I opened it. Against the gusts that wrapped around the building, baying like a wild animal, I lowered Mathilda into an old stroller and harnessed her in. She was sleeping. Once inside, I drew her alongside the doctor's desk and took a seat. I realized what it must have looked like. There I was, relaying the collapse and subsequent visit to the ER room in Bournemouth, Mathilda's night terrors, and the daytime sleepiness that never left her refreshed. I told him that there were other things: she was weak and sometimes couldn't walk in the mornings, that her words sounded shaky, slurred even. More frightening than anything was the fact that her personality had changed, that she was shutting down, and I sometimes couldn't reach her. When he placed the cold ring of his stethoscope against her chest, she didn't so much as stir. Her reflexes were normal, she did not have a fever, her blood pressure and pulse were unremarkable. There was nothing for him to see other than a three-year old child taking a late afternoon nap in a stroller. Not many doctors would blame him for writing a referral back to Dr. Fitzwilliam, Ear Nose and Throat Consultant, smiling weakly as he showed us the door.

"She's a real sleeping beauty," he said, his voice trailing behind me as I moved toward the exit, back into a place of defeated isolation.

That same night Oliver and I put the kids to bed before setting ourselves up with a movie, shutting out the world and the driving rain that beat hard on our bedroom window. For a while, the house fell silent to the night, pulling darkness over our street while we zoned out, watching images flick across the laptop. Then, not much later, and without warning, Mathilda appeared, wobbling on Oliver's side of the bed.

"Hey. You okay?" he said.

"I'm floppy. My ankles hurt," she replied.

"Let's see. Come up here and we'll take a look."

"Is Emily here?" she asked.

"No. It's nighttime. See how dark it is outside?"

"I haven't played with her for ages," she replied, before Oliver caught her head bobbing as she tried to climb up on the bed. He lifted her weak body on to his lap and under the bedsheets. I reached for her ankles. There was nothing to see. A moment later we both felt a warm wetting on the sheet below us, and I asked Mathilda whether she needed the bathroom. She shook her head before giving into the ir-resistible urge to sleep again. With the realization of another symptom, Oliver and I looked at each other. As if biting my lip could in anyway control my emotions, I closed my eyes on tears that were already falling.

"Let's take her back in to hospital," he said.

9 CATCH HER WHEN SHE FALLS
April 15th 2010

> "But no one except Lucy knew that as it circled the
> mast it had whispered to her, "courage dear heart"
> and the voice, she felt sure, was Aslan and with the
> voice a delicious smell breathed in her face."
>
> —**C.S Lewis**
> ***Voyage of the Dawn Treader***

The anesthetist who brought Mathilda around from the
MRI scan reassured me that she would most likely sleep
for the next 5 hours. The odd thing was that even then,
I doubted it. Coming out of that anesthesia did allow her
some minutes of rest, it seemed, but by the time we were
back on the ward she was awake and distressed. Somewhere
between keeping her from waking the other children in our
bay and tugging at the needle in her hand, I wrestled with
what Dr. Anthony Jensen had told us a few hours ago—
about not bullshitting us, about the prospect of Mathilda
having a cerebellar tumor. It was 5 a.m. by the time I drifted
off into a fitful sleep beside her in my own cot-bed when I
heard a blood-curdling shriek from nowhere. It was so intense that I, too, must have called out as I leapt up to comfort her. A nurse came rushing in to the bay, asking what

was going on, and then taking Mathilda's temperature. It was normal, but the two of us were not, and later, I saw the nurse's comment on the notes at the end of the bed. The patient was "difficult," it read.

The fact that Dr. Jensen and the neurology team did not share the results of the MRI until lunchtime the following day reassured me. He had asked the radiologist reporting on Mathilda's scan to call him in the small hours if it showed a lesion of any kind, "Even if it's 4 in the morning, I want to know," he said. I had "no news is good news" telephone reports for Oliver and my sister, and the morning passed uneventfully. Two sweet young women, no older than twenty, came to our bedside. They were volunteer play therapists, and they presented Mathilda with a box of Barbie dolls, along with an hour of their time to sit with her and dress and act out the perfect figures. Mathilda was alert enough to engage with the two angels. Their supervision meant I could grab a shower on the ward and allow the hot running water to draw me back into a world where normal people wash on normal days.

When the neurology team finally walked into the ward, they were all smiles. I sensed the normal scan results were unexpected on their part and this left little by way of conversation between us. At that point, Dr. Jensen's lack of interest barely touched me; I was preoccupied with relief. The rope I had seen in my mind's eye the previous night, still fresh in my mind, felt like it had been pulled up a little—with me clinging on. The two of us were still dangling over a precipice, but the danger of losing my grip was no longer imminent. Mathilda did not have a cerebellar tumor. There was something else affecting her, but I hoped against everything that, whatever it was, it wasn't something that would kill her.

What did come as a surprise, however, was our immediate discharge. I understood the model of socialized health care, and that discharge planning takes place once you are admitted and staff are under pressure to reduce the cost of any given admission. Yet, I pointed out that Mathilda was the same child I had brought in several days back. She was not diagnosed. She was not treated. She was not better. We were supposed to wait six weeks for notification of an appointment as outpatients, all the while caring for her twenty-four hours a day and watching her deteriorate. It was hard to wrap my head around how a sick child, who should be further investigated, could be discharged after one test that eliminated one theory. It was even harder to return to the ongoing exhaustion that endangered our family balance as Oliver and I worked out how to manage her care both day and night, hold down a job and educate the older two children whilst protecting them from the emotional fallout that surrounded us. I looked at Dr. Jensen in disbelief. "You may be sending her home," I said irritably, "but she is the same sick child I brought in here two days ago. Whatever is wrong with her is neurological and is a twenty-four-hour problem."

That first night at Bristol Children's hospital marked us both out. There was a fine line between being a caring, responsible parent and an intense, over-anxious one. Without a diagnosis or a clear-cut clinical presentation, we were already in danger of being boxed up into a clinical casket in which neither of us belonged. That hospital admission was the first of many times we would battle to prove our daughter was physically, not mentally, ill, and needed further investigations. In the meantime, we were sent home.

As the daily routine of our lives became centered around Mathilda's needs, all I could do was place a pile of school books on the kitchen table each morning and have Libby and Elliot work through them until lunch time. Friends came and went, picking them up for a run in the woods with our home-school group on Tuesdays, or sitting with me in the lounge where Mathilda was invariably sleeping, then awake crying, then sleeping again. Libby and Elliot were able to make their own snacks, sometimes lunch. I do not remember the two of them complaining when I was unavailable to help them with their work, yet there were times when they completed their tasks in a retreated silence.

They continued with the games they loved playing as affectionately as they had always done, and I comforted myself with the notion of "healthy neglect." I could no longer print out project supplies the night before or have a group of kids over for Nerf war, but I leaned on the hope that they were learning a different set of skills: self-educating independence. To stop Mathilda from injuring herself, Liberty learned to carry her sister and support her body when she became floppy in the dining chair. I served up supper in the meanwhile or attended to phone calls and essential household tasks. Elliot would ask what he could do to help, and he accepted graciously the new limitations on our social life. Being an extrovert, that was hard for him.

Despite living in what I felt was a constant state of crisis, I was aware of having to transform myself into a different kind of parent—one that could cope with caring for an ill child both day and night and maintain a sense of normality for everyone else. I tried my best to hide my fears from the three of them, but the full weight of not knowing what was wrong with her and wondering what new symptom might be thrown at us that week bore down on me hard. Tears were as close as an opened bottle of white wine. I did not like what I was becoming. I was never labile and was not used to feeling out of control. Much of my emotional fragility lay within my body's layers of exhaustion, the result of entire nights spent at Mathilda's side, whispering words of love and reassurance of our presence, and comforting her the times she cried out she was "breaking to pieces." In those moments, I felt as though someone had stuck their hand right inside my chest, twisted their fingers around my heart, and ripped it out. It was beyond anything I had ever experienced before, and her words made me question the purpose of it all.

Suffering changes things. And it was changing my view of God because our little girl was being dragged in and out of dark places that we could not access. We did not even know where to look, and in the isolating hours between midnight and dawn, we frequently felt she was gone from us, pulled away to some distant land of pain and terror—of torture. There was no way of explaining to her what she was going through. My instincts told me her illness was neurological in origin, and that her brain wasn't functioning properly. She was three years old, old enough to articulate her thoughts. Yet young enough, I prayed, that whatever was happening, she wouldn't remember it.

Several weeks after our discharge from the hospital, there was an incident on the stairs. Elliot was arranging a Playmobil castle with Noah's ark across the corn-colored carpet of Liberty and Elliot's bedroom. He was talking away to himself and ready for some company. I watched Mathilda crawl up the stairs, leaning on her hands on the step above.

Seeing her through the slats in the banister, Elliot called for her to join him.

"Are you ready to play? It's a great game...come on Mimi!"

"Coming Els," she responded, climbing up on all fours slowly, her head bobbing up and down rhythmically.

It was not often, that we heard her sweet voice; when we did, it was delightful. I stood at the bottom to make sure Mathilda made it all the way up, and I saw her glance sideways to the bedroom, where her brother and the dozens of small, lined-up figures were poised for play. We did not know it then, but it was the sheer delight of the moment, the joy of the invitation and the anticipation of "the game" that had her knees sagging to a full collapse. Down she came like a bag of potatoes. I grabbed her before she hit the floor. Elliot stood staring over the banister, peering down, wondering if what he said had somehow been the cause of her injuries. Months later, we would come to understand what triggered her collapses. At that point, we only knew that she could drop down at anytime, anywhere, and that we needed to be right there to catch her whenever she fell.

With a new bruise on her temple, we returned to our GP as I had done the week before. If accessing the team at Bristol Children's hospital was virtually impossible, we could at least see one of the doctors at Fishponds Family Practice regularly. Each time I carried Mathilda in, we saw a different doctor, and each time I choked on tears, reiterating her floppiness, her slurred speech and her bizarre inability to maintain sleep at night. This time, I offered up my own diagnostic suggestions. Could it be Lyme disease? A tick had bitten Mathilda, after all, during our year in Princeton. One evening after having played in the woods, we laughed when she told us around the table that there was a spider in her belly button—until she lifted her top and revealed an engorged tick that had buried itself under her skin. Could she be infected from that bite? On an earlier visit, clutching at straws, I questioned leukemia. She was excessively sleepy and had pain in her joints.

"It isn't leukemia, or Lyme's," Dr. Bledsoe reassured me during a visit in which I sat, trying to hold it together. "Her blood results are normal. I am sorry. We don't know exactly what's wrong with her, Claire. I wish I could help. The only thing I can do is bring her case up at the meeting tomorrow," he said.

On this last occasion, Dr. Larsen, fully abreast of the nature of our previous visits, was concerned enough to push through the recent referral to ENT. In her letter, she requested an *"urgent review of this delightful three-year old,"* stating that, *"she is waking up between 30 and 40 times a night, and that the impact of her lack of sleep could not be overstated. It is affecting Mathilda's behavior, co-ordination, continence and motor function."* The same letter indicated *"her mother is extremely sensible and absolutely at the end of her tether."* With the normal MRI, neurological assessments and blood results behind us, there was a lot of room for self-doubt, and there were times I wondered how ill Mathilda really was. The lines were blurring, and in the small doctor's office with Mathilda asleep, looking plump and peaceful, I had a very hard time describing her symptoms, particularly the nights. It was profoundly important to me to communicate accurately what a 24-hour period looked like. In so doing, I was aware as coming across as the one who was unraveling. Dr. Larsen took my visit seriously enough to write the letter right then and there.

My fears, however, converged upon each doctor's lack of knowledge and clear diagnosis of Mathilda's symptoms. In the throes of swinging back and forth within the national health system, between pediatric teams and family practitioners, we were slipping through every clinical net there was. Mathilda was declining, and we remained in isolated ignorance.

10 "WHAT'S COMMON IS COMMON"
April 25th 2010

"The matter with human beans," the BFG went on, "is that they absolutely refusing to believe in anything unless they is actually seeing it right in front of their own schnozzles."

—Roald Dahl
The BFG

Ten days later, Mathilda was readmitted to Ward 36. Her ataxic gait had worsened, causing her to fall more frequently. And there was another addition to the myriad of symptoms—one that drove us back to the ER room. Throughout any given day, she began to roll and poke her tongue around the inside of her bottom lip, seemingly without control. Sometimes it would coincide with her head bobbing up and down. I couldn't figure out what triggered this tongue thrusting, and I had no idea if this was now a permanent new feature or not. Apart from anything else, this changed her facial appearance dramatically but I was more concerned about how it was affecting her speech, which sounded wobbly and quiet, like that of a frail old lady. This was yet another way that she was changing. With each new symptom, Mathilda withdrew further into her own world, with the distance giving rise to a profound absence felt by all. There were times when she was angry and frustrated at the slurring of her words, her inability to keep up with other children, or her inescapable surrendering to sleep. This was understandable, as were the tears that came at the slightest displeasure, making every wakeful hour a roller-coaster of emotional stress.

But as the trauma of each night piled up, a frightening thing grew inside her—vacancy. Some days it seemed as though she was thousands of miles away. To counteract the overwhelming sense of losing essentially who she was, we all maintained physical contact while playing with her, even if she couldn't fully respond. It was our way of staying connected. We would insist on eye contact and kiss her face, hoping we could stimulate a reaction, maybe even hear her laugh. Libby would tickle her on the rug in the lounge, knowing that Mathilda couldn't reciprocate, but holding and rolling around with her anyway.

The tongue thrusting gradually replaced all her smiles, and it seemed that this part of her was gone forever. Despite trying hard to keep my anxiety under control, there was one morning after Oliver had left for work when Liberty saw me crying as I reheated coffee in the microwave. Standing there, in the kitchen, I regretted voicing my fears since it is an awful burden for a ten-year-old to support her parent through a crisis. Yet I recognized in Liberty something of my former self, an inherent emotional strength that could grasp the facts without crumbling. However, it was times like these that I felt I was beginning to fail the older children too. Until then, I had been able to hide my concerns from them, for the most part, but the deepening weariness rendered me transparent. Libby slipped her arms around my waist.

"Am I making this all up? Is there something wrong with Mathilda?" I asked her, peering down into my mug.

"No Mum. You are not making it up," she said. "There is something wrong. It's just that the doctors don't know what it is. No one does."

"I'm beginning to wonder if any of this is really as bad as it seems," I muttered, because for the first time, the edges between reality and imagination were beginning to blur.

"But you need to know that if this was happening to you or Elliot, I would cry the same amount of tears. And I wouldn't give up until we found out what was wrong with you." Libby leaned her head in against my arm.

"I will help you, Mum," she said. "As much as I can."

I trusted her judgment, then, for she was seeing it all. If I was honest, self-doubt was taking hold. When I allowed myself to feel the full impact of Mathilda's illness, whatever it was, I wanted to doubt my own grasp of the situation. It was an attractive option—that it was my brain's malfunctioning, not Mathilda's, that was really in question. What brought me back, however, was that every time I turned round, I, too, saw Mathilda trying to stand, to sleep, to walk, and to speak, tongue thrusting whenever she tried. Every new symptom brought with it its own terror; my heart sank at the prospect of further testing and time in hospital. I didn't want to take her back, but I knew I should.

Going with the theory that she had sleep apnea, Mathilda underwent a basic sleep study on the second night. We were in the same bed as before, by the window, when a large nurse called Chelsea came in and set down an old-fashioned black electrical box. Plastic nasal cannula were inserted in her nostrils and a probe was attached to her pinky. Figuring out the leads to the box proved more challenging for the young woman who looked like she might have just left school. I kept my thoughts to myself and remained focused on Mathilda, who had already begun her routine of dream, wake, thrash about, sleep, dream, cry, wake. Now, she began pulling the transparent tubes away from her face.

"Take them out Mumma," she complained in waves. "I can't breathe with them in my nose."

"We need to keep them in, just for tonight. It's so the doctors can understand why you're having a hard time sleeping," I replied, hoping reason might work. The procedure itself was not especially invasive, but Mathilda was so volatile that any added discomfort would be enough to push her into non-cooperation. Another nurse stepped inside the curtains and admitted to never having performed one of these tests before. Eventually, after 20 minutes or so she succeeded attaching the leads from Mathilda's head and hands to the black box and the nasal cannula which wound behind her ears and was taped to both cheeks. To combat Mathilda's attempts at undoing their work, Chelsea bandaged her tiny wrists into rigid splints before tucking each arm under the sheets which were pulled tightly by both nurses working on either side of the bed. I was confident neither in the device nor in Mathilda's compliance, nor in the nurses' expertise. However, I felt a strange reassurance that, if any new symptoms emerged, at least we were already here.

The next morning she was transferred. The bed was needed for another child, and I was asked to take Mathilda across the hospital to Ward 30, which I wrongly assumed was the neurology unit. Before packing our belongings, I walked over to the nurse's station and stood beside the black box on the high counter. The thick leads were still wrapped around it, and a yellow post—it note on the top recorded Mathilda's name and date of birth. I asked when we might have the results from the night's sleep test, choosing my words carefully so I would not come off as demanding.

"It needs to be analyzed," one of the nurses replied. "We

can't say when you will get the results."

"When they do come through, will they be sent over to Ward 30?" I asked, hoping that the test would be interpreted on site and that we would have the results by the end of the week.

"We'll try. Can't promise," she said.

"Were you able to tell from the data if there was anything abnormal going on last night?" I enquired gently.

"Not really. No. We don't usually do these. And anyway, we still need to find out where to send it," she said, turning away and reaching for the phone. Deflated, and sensing the obvious irritation in her voice, I walked away from the nurse's station and the black box, which I imagined would remain there for hours, days even.

Knowing a ward transfer meant another full round of questions, triage tests and a certain level of compliance on Mathilda's part, I took her along to the play center for a break. It was a small room on the top floor, staffed by volunteers, with donated toys, craft supplies and the latest video game technology. Surprisingly alert that morning, Mathilda chose to play with a frail-looking girl of roughly the same age, balding from her last dose of chemotherapy. Most parents sat outside on the roof terrace where town houses abutted the hospital so closely you could see directly into their bedrooms unless they happen to have kept the curtains drawn. On benches with inscriptions of donors, of families honoring the memory of the child they lost, those of us who still had children to care for soaked in the sunshine, the relief of fresh air and of volunteers engaging with our kids. The daylight and the throb of traffic below provided a tenuous link to the outside world, wherein people commuted to work and thought about what to eat for supper. But the children with their drips, walking aids and other obvious marks of sickness reminded us that our existence was elsewhere, that we belonged here with them and with their faulty bodies.

"What's wrong with your daughter?" one mother asked me.

"We don't know," I answered quietly. "She's been tested for a brain tumor but that came back negative. Another test was done last night to see if she has sleep apnea."

"She don't look too bad. My son's got scars up and down his front. He's just about to have another operation on his bowel," she said, looking down at her bitten fingernails.

"I'm sorry to hear that," I replied, my brow furrowed in concern. I was sorry. There we were, connected strangers in a place we didn't want to be, with our children hooked to IV lines, feeding tubes and dressed wounds, struggling to do what all children do—play.

As I stood up from the bench and peered inside, I noticed Mathilda's knees give out as she began to dress herself in an elaborate princess costume, one of her favorite games.

Unable to hold the tension in her legs, she dropped down to her knees and crawled toward the doll house just a few feet away, her arm motioning the bald girl to follow. The two slowly moved furniture around the rooms and brought the tiny figures to life with their high-pitched, reedy voices. Watching Mathilda across the room, with her head dipping up and down on her chest, just then it struck me that her movements resembled those of a bobble-head toy. The ones you see perched in the back of cars.

The pediatric medical ward was identical in layout to the short stay unit, with six beds to a bay, a main nurse's station and various rooms to accommodate medications, equipment and laundry. Except for a few en-suite bedrooms for seriously ill children, bathrooms were always shared. Several qualified nurses oversaw the running of the ward, although the bulk of the work was shouldered by unqualified staff wearing brightly patterned uniforms and colorful name badges. As with every other ward, the minutes of each day seemed defined by the predictable sound of trays sliding in and out of the food trolley and the odor of overheated meals. Beyond that, time was marked by the four hourly vitals checks. We waited out the long hours, not knowing if, or when, a doctor would show up.

The next morning, not long after Oliver arrived,

Mathilda was visited by Dr. Fitzwilliam, the pediatric ENT consultant who, it seemed, hadn't changed since we last saw him 18 months ago; he had declared her fit and well to travel and formally discharged her from his care. Along with two new, dashing young male ENT colleagues who swept around the pediatric wards together, they were known amongst staff and parents as "The Three Amigos."

Dr. Fitzilliam, a leader in his field, maintained his effortless bedside manner, which immediately put us both at ease. We were glad to see him again, although by then I was convinced her problem was neurological. If that were true, he would not be able to help us this time. Surprised to see us, Dr. Fitzwilliam explained that the neurology team had asked for his opinion in order to rule out obstructive sleep apnea. Mathilda had not wanted to change out of her floral pink pajamas and was lying down when he approached her bed. After looking down her throat, he told us her tonsils were a normal size, but he would remove them if we wanted him to. Since neither of us wished to consent to an invasive procedure that wasn't necessary, both of us declined his offer. The sleep study results that may or may not have confirmed sleep apnea, he said, were not available to him. He'd not been able to track them down. Perhaps they were lost within the system, perhaps within the old black box itself. Even so, the three amigos were confident that sleep apnea was not the problem, and equally confident that the sleep data wouldn't show up any time soon. Genuinely sorry they could not help, the consultation ended without any further insight. Dr. Fitzwilliam had, however, eliminated another possible condition. And that, in its own way, felt like progress.

By the time the sun had set behind the west side of the city, Mathilda was visited by Martin Jones, another senior neurologist, and half of the young team, with whom we were now familiar. Dr. Jones was an older man, slender and lined, yet there was a lightness about him, a sense of fun. To compensate for his extreme height, he would take off his white coat, bend low as he spoke to his small patients, and find something to talk about. Picking up Mathilda's Piglet on the bed, he began chatting about how Winnie-the-Pooh was his favorite film, as if he'd seen it recently. She smiled weakly, but he sensed it was not enough for her to warm up to him. He stood up and gestured for us to follow him out of the ward.

"I would like us to look at Mathilda's walking. Let's go to the outpatients' area where there's more space," he said. "Will she do that for us?"

"We can carry her there and see she what she's up for," I replied, not knowing how much energy she would have or whether she would handle another examination. As Oliver lifted Mathilda from the bed, we followed the doctors into a large, deserted waiting area. Evidence of a full day's activity at the clinic lay in the scattered toys and trash covering several of the seats. Dr. Jones turned on the lights, and we began recounting the complex and confusing array of symptoms as they had presented themselves over the last few months, and why it was becoming increasingly difficult to care for Mathilda at home. She was as alert as we could hope for, initially doing as she was asked, walking across the room in an almost straight line, skipping and jumping slowly. It took enormous effort, and she wobbled on occasion, but her ataxia was mild that day, which complicated the clinical picture and left the team perplexed. When they asked her to hop on one leg, her opposite knee wouldn't lift, and her head began to bob. As Mathilda refused to perform all the tricks a second time around, her grumpiness and lethargy only muddied the diagnostic waters further. She wouldn't even try. I could tell her unwillingness to comply with the hand-eye coordination tests or to describe what it was that made her roll her tongue around her bottom lip was becoming a source of frustration for the team. They had little to go on.

We gave up and took her back to the ward. Dr. Jones pressed Oliver and I further for details, relying solely on our side of the story. He wanted to try one more thing. While Mathilda stood between us in front of the locker by her bed with her small hands inside ours, he suddenly reached down toward her and tickled her under the arms. This surprised us all. Mathilda immediately pulled away from him and hung back behind Oliver's legs. Then she began to cry.

"We can rule out narcolepsy," he remarked. "If she had narcolepsy she would have fallen down just then."

"Really? What is narcolepsy?" Oliver asked as he helped Mathilda back into bed.

"It's a sleep disorder that makes you collapse when you are happy. So when I tickled her, she would have fallen. She's too young for it, anyway," he said, wanting to wrap the conversation up. "Besides, it usually runs in families, and neither of you have it do you?"

"So where do we go from here?" I said, not wishing to linger on a condition that was irrelevant.

"What is common is common," Dr. Jones said. He went on to expound his theory—we should look for the most likely condition after a brain tumor and sleep apnea, and work our way slowly down the list. The next disorder to eliminate, he said, would be epilepsy. I already had my doubts that Mathilda's was not an ordinary case. Considering what he'd said, I put narcolepsy out of my mind. My more pressing fears lay with the reality that we were on borrowed time with every hospital admission. If this last assessment and the black box did not yield an answer, it was back home for us, with or without a diagnosis, prognosis or the hope of treatment.

11 UNRAVELING
Early May 2010

"True courage is in facing danger
when you are most afraid."

—Frank Baum
The Wizard of Oz

What Oliver and I went home with that day was not the reassurance that Mathilda had neither sleep apnea nor narcolepsy. Whilst imagining the worst, we were left to care for her unnamed needs beneath dark clouds of uncertainty. As far I was concerned, the hospital stay had been anything but successful. We were also feeling estranged from Liberty and Elliot, and drove directly to collect them from Wendy, who had offered to care for them while Mathilda was in hospital. Knowing how disruptive the previous admission had been for them, I let go of worrying whether or not they had kept up with their schoolwork over the past few days. It was a lot to ask.

Wendy ran her home of four young children as the captain of a tight ship on a purposeful voyage. She was organized, driven, dedicated and determined. More than anything, she squeezed every second out of every minute of the day, and she expected the same of those around her. Her five-year old Emily could feed the baby, Hannah the eldest could prepare breakfast for the family, and I saw Heather, then six, clean the kitchen on more than one occasion like a professional whilst Wendy took a bath. Beyond giving them the skills to run a household, she also made sure they had access to some of the best academic material and a wealth of great books. Glyn, Wendy's husband, had transformed their narrow, winding hallway into a library where classic children's stories were within arm's reach of the girls' bedroom.

Despite her ambition for the children, her methods were always sprinkled with love and kindness. I knew Liberty and Elliot were in good hands when staying there. The two of them had adapted quickly to her military-style routine, which on this particular visit involved a morning of de-stoning plums from a neighbor's tree. There was a year's supply of plum jam to be made. Nothing in Wendy's life was ever wasted.

Turning up at the bungalow where everyone under the roof contributed to the regular rhythm of family life, I was struck by the contrast between home life and the world we had just come from. I could not quite shake off the fact that the children's hospital was always full; never was there an empty bed. Just a few miles away, there was an overwhelming number of children and parents who were suffering in some way. I started to add up the odds of actually having a well and robust child, and with this skewed perspective dominating my thoughts, I gratefully thanked Wendy for handing back our two healthy children. On her doorstep, I held both Liberty and Elliot that much longer before asking them to jump in the car and buckle up. Emily came to the door and asked if Mathilda would come in and play, now that she was out of hospital.

"How did it go?" Wendy asked. "Have they figured out what's wrong?"

"I don't think so. Except we know it's not sleep apnea or narcolepsy," I replied, pained that Mathilda was too exhausted to play. I didn't know what else to say, other than repeating my thanks.

"Liberty and Elliot are amazing Claire. They did all their school work and chores without complaining." I was momentarily lifted by what she said. Yet, if I had accepted her offer for us all to come in and stay for supper, I would have broken down.

Driving back through the winding lanes of Winterbourne and into the edges of the city where our house lay within earshot of the M32, I felt secure in the knowledge that we were all together, despite Oliver's approaching flight to the US to present a paper. I was not sure how I would get through the nights alone with him gone. By now, the only routine I could realistically sustain was one where we were almost entirely housebound. Nevertheless, I prided myself on the fact that his trip in a few days was a vote of confidence in my abilities to cope with the new circumstances life had thrown at us.

We had sat down a few nights earlier, and between the two of us, we thrashed out how best to manage home life whilst he continued to hold down his job at the university. Mathilda's needs now demanded full time care over a twenty-four-hour period, which was more than what one person could handle. On any given night, we were still averaging less than two hours of broken sleep. In addition to her terrifying nightmares, we were medicating her every few hours for the pain in her ankles and wrists. When the dreams demanded her escape, we would hold her tight, attempting to prevent her from throwing herself out of bed or against the wall. She had also stopped eating with us at meal times, which left her ravenous at night, with one of us trotting downstairs to find something suitable to eat.

One morning in the kitchen, she lost her equilibrium near the open dishwasher door, where the upturned cutlery missed her head by inches. Oliver had placed the stair gate as a safety measure again after she had fallen from the top to the bottom. These near misses meant I couldn't take my eyes off her unless she was sleeping—the only time I had to catch up on tasks such as meal preparation, housework, and being with Libby and Elliot. While awake, Mathilda needed carrying from one room to another if she was feeling weak. Then, one moment you could be talking to her, and the next, you would turn round and she was gone, as if someone had shut off the lights. It could be anywhere, anytime.

The worry of not educating Liberty and Elliot properly concerned us too, but with zero savings to fall back on, and with Oliver in the midst of a three-year middle management position, taking a break from work so that we both could be home was not an option. We discussed enrolling them in school again, but decided it would be another disruptive change, and somewhere in the back of our minds there was a faint hope that all this might pass. Our parents lived over two hours away, and my newly-wed sister was working whilst raising a lively toddler in London. All my local mom friends already had their own broods to deal with. For now, other than shouldering the bulk of it, it was hard to see how we could divide Mathilda's care in such a way as to give Oliver the strength to get through the next day's teaching and administration on top of a four-mile cycle ride to and from his office. If I could give him a block of sleep each night until the summer when he would have more flexibility with his schedule, we could make it work. We arranged a shift system for the next six weeks where he would stay with Mathilda until midnight, allowing me a few hours' sleep before I took over. I would then nurse her in her room until the morning and start the day over with the three of them.

Beyond that, neither of us had any idea what our lives would be like—how, or if, Mathilda might deteriorate further. I was already concerned about the emotional toll our situation was taking on Oliver. Psoriasis broke out on his hands, cracking the skin and opening up in wounds; his eyes were permanently bloodshot. He looked wrecked. Most nights he came home from work wound up like a spring, caught in the wranglings of middle management, which bore its own pressures and frustrations. He was first and foremost a scholar, and by his own admission, he found all aspects of administration tedious. The management role had been thrust upon him at a time when drastic changes were being made to higher education in the UK. A number of his colleagues had lost their jobs. Through promotion to associate professor he was now in a position of responsibility, yet without authority, where he would have to execute decisions that he had no say in, and with which he often did not agree. Groaning under the weight of juggling a full teaching load, supervising PhD students, and writing and traveling, the endless meetings of middle management felt like a harrowing sentence to him. But it was nothing compared to the gravity of our unraveling situation at home.

With the two of us experiencing a new level of exhaustion he was also concerned about how I was holding up. Tears seemed to drop out of me even when performing the most mundane of tasks, like vacuuming. I had also broken out in unsightly welts across my chest the night we were told Mathilda might have a brain tumor. They looked a lot like irregular fibrous scars, each an inch long. Nothing I put on them would make them heal, and each week thereafter, more appeared, migrating to my back and thighs. Although I had never done this before, I had begun counting the minutes around 6 p.m. until I heard the garage door swing open, where Oliver would park his bike. As soon as the squeaking of hinges was heard, the kids would announce his return and rush to the back door. I would allow myself to breathe a little deeper, moving the half-empty bottle of wine to the back of the counter behind the paper towel roll.

Oliver coped by compartmentalizing his life. When he was at work, he focused on the task before him, with the exception of calling me several times a day to check how we all were. When he was home, we had all his attention. This had not always been the case, but it was another way in which things were shifting.

I began reordering some of the details of our domestic lives. For a $5 service fee, once a week Tesco's delivered all our food directly to the kitchen table in order to avoid carrying Mathilda around the grocery store. She was putting on a noticeable amount of weight, which made transferring her challenging. She was also too floppy and sleepy for the supermarket cart seat. The home delivery of food with just a few clicks of a button allowed me to keep the cupboards full and to place a decent meal on the table each night.

For the first time ever in Libby and Elliot's education, I started relying on textbooks and reading as the main form of learning rather than directed teaching, elaborate projects, field trips and co-op classes. Instead of reading out loud, I bought audio-tapes and played them during quiet time after lunch, somehow still determined to keep up with the curriculum for that year. Realistically, I no longer had the energy for printing out worksheets, reading lists and chore charts the night beforehand. That all went. Despite the turbulence in their lives, the two of them managed to plow through the pile of workbooks I plopped down on the table once they cleared the breakfast dishes away. Liberty began helping Elliot with his math before picking up the violin and doubling her practice time, opening the lounge windows for all passersby to hear. Elliot became quiet. He stopped asking me for things, taking all his requests to his older sister instead.

When we were desperate for a change of scenery, occasionally we attended various meet–ups with friends, where managing Mathilda amounted to her remaining in the stroller. I would find a place to sit down, and there she could sleep, oblivious of where we were or what we were doing. Wednesday afternoons were an opportunity for the home-school children of Bristol to come together at the local sports center. Libby and Elliot were enthusiastic about the multi-sports program since most of their friends participated, and they all jumped into the pool afterwards. It was good, clean fun—what sweet childhood memories were made of. Having missed many of the recent weeks, I was determined to drive the kids there, no matter how bad things were. Looking back, I cannot imagine why I signed up Mathilda for a private swim class that week. Perhaps it was denial, or a deep-seated desire to turn back the clock on our situation and maintain some kind of normality. Either way, I was abruptly brought to my senses during her lesson when her teacher asked her to float on her back for a few seconds. Out of the corner of my eye, and from half way across the pool where I was swimming laps, I saw she had fallen asleep—in five feet of water.

The worst part of getting out of the house was engaging with friends. Some were exceptional in their ongoing support, yet for the most part, I sensed a pervasive silence and withdrawal from other families who knew us well. I imagined they were at a loss for words, but their reticence left me feeling judged, as if I had somehow gone off the deep end. Their silence left me bewildered, vulnerable and hurt. More than that, it added further to my growing sense of isolation.

Thankfully, there were several exceptions. Sam, who

lived around the corner, checked in with me almost daily, and always with the reassurance that she and her family were sending up prayers for answers and healing. Her constant care was a gift. Wendy's kitchen became a place where I could be completely honest, knowing that however much I lamented and expressed my anger and frustration, I was safe. Often I talked, relaying the latest challenge, or I just cried, confessing to doubting whether I could suffer through another night of watching Mathilda hallucinate and scream with the pain in her legs. But in those days before the final diagnosis that would make some, if not complete, sense of her suffering, I myself was pleading for God to respond, to relieve the torment she was in.

The most significant of these afternoons is etched in my memory. After making tea, Wendy closed the kitchen door on our collective seven children. I repeated something she had heard me say before. It was a prayer of sorts, more of a demand, perhaps, that I spoke out loud whilst she busied herself around the kitchen. Until that point, we had seen Mathilda retreating further and further into her own world with each passing week. This deepening withdrawal, coupled with the barrage of bizarre symptoms and what I felt to be God's silence left me terrified. From a providential perspective, it was quite possible that Mathilda's diagnosis might be of a terminal nature. I was acutely aware of that. But I also knew that I was too physically, and spiritually,

fragile to face it. That if we were to lose her, the grief inflicted on all of us would be something I would carry from
her cradle to my grave. She was my child. On a human level, the suffering and potential prognosis seemed not only
senseless, but somehow cruel. Where was the good in it?
Where was God in it? What was the purpose behind the
depths of her suffering? Falling short of these answers, and
reverently respecting that all things were in God's hand, all
I could do, as a mother, was beg.

As Wendy allowed me to rant that day, I was not
fully aware of what I was saying. I remember hitting the
table with my fist, spilling the cup of tea. And in a moment,
I screamed out loud—that it was enough, I couldn't do it!
I couldn't watch her anymore. Then and there, I pleaded
with God to finally listen, to stop His silence, and to change
the trajectory she was on. I begged Him to give her, not a
terminal disease, but a disorder we could deal with, one that
would not take her completely away. If prayer has the power
to change the course of our lives, I think that moment was
it. Beyond the sound of the rain beating down on the windows, there was nothing more in that humble kitchen than
two women—one supportive, carrying her friend through
dark days, the other collapsing at breaking point.

Something turned in that hour. God's ear acknowledged my brokenness in my desperation. I am convinced, as
a result, that Mathilda's life was spared. Within a fortnight

of that plea, there would be answers. Perhaps not what Oliver and I expected, but answers nonetheless, signaling not a demise, but a deterioration we could, in time, cope with.

Soon after that, Mathilda was called in for an EEG (electroencephalogram) to test the electrical activity of her brain. Eliminating epilepsy was the next condition on the list of possibilities. The test itself was fairly simple, although it was hard to get her to stay awake long enough to glue a dozen electrodes to her scalp. I was able to reassure her that, this time, we would be going straight home afterwards. The need for her to remain awake during 20-minute intervals while prompted by the technician made her utterly miserable. I helped him coax Mathilda into a semblance of compliance. Toward the end of the study, he admitted to never having seen a child so sleepy in his 15 years of practice.

Several days later, it was confirmed that her problem was not epilepsy, and that there had, in fact, been 'no definite abnormality found.' We were still on track with Dr. Jones' theory of "what's common is common," and I wondered what would come next after this.

By the time Oliver flew to Princeton, New Jersey, to present his paper, and after the swimming incident that left Mathilda asleep in five feet of water, I was losing confidence in our situation. Physically, I could keep lines of communication open with our friends and family. I could run the house and hear the older two recite the poems they had learned. I could sit and alter some of Liberty's old clothes to fit her younger sister. But that was about it. In every other way our lives were unrecognizable, and I could no longer escape a nagging reality that Mathilda was sick—really sick. In the past few days she had needed help getting on and off the toilet since her muscle tone was too low to maintain her balance, or wipe herself or pull up her pants. Whatever was affecting her body was neither normal nor natural. Together with my unwillingness to accept what was happening, this realization impelled me to pick up the phone and call my parents.

"I'm taking Mathilda back in," I said.

"Why? What's going on? Is she worse? Do you need us to come and stay?" Mum asked.

"There's no rush and there's nothing more than…" My throat was tightening. "It's just so abnormal. None of it makes any sense. Perhaps plan on staying a few days, if you and Dad don't mind." Mum detected the determination in my voice and said they would drive down first thing in the morning. She handed Dad the phone, and repeated what I had said to him.

"We can come whenever you want," he said. "Maybe the best way to think about it is that now you have a new normal," he added. I knew he was trying to help me understand the situation, to rationalize in order to cope, but there was not a bone in me that wanted to hear, or accept, what he said.

I spoke to Oliver via Skype that same day about my decision to return to the hospital with Mathilda the next morning. He was calling from our friends' house in Princeton. That night, the Bowlins were throwing a get-together for Oliver, and the place was alive with people's voices moving around in the kitchen. They lived on the Circle, where we had stayed during our time in Princeton. With large, bay windows, their home boasted a year-round view of the woods. I had sat in the lounge many times with my friend Mimi and I remembered watching the children play in the snow, pointing out with delight various footprints, convincing each other that some of them belonged to a bear.

The sound of people talking made it hard for him to hear me clearly, and I detected a note of frustration. Earlier that visit, he had explained Mathilda's deterioration to them and our lack of progress with the doctors. Mimi had offered to put us in touch with her sister in the US, a pediatric neurologist who herself had lost a two-year-old daughter to a progressive neurological disorder some years ago.

"If there is nothing new," he said, "why take her back?"

"There are some new things. She is experiencing strange sensations in her feet when she touches uneven surfaces, like out on the back patio and on grass. I don't know why, but it makes her scream and lose her calm. She's so far from being right, and we are still six weeks away from an outpatient's appointment. It's too far off."

"Can't you wait? Until I get home?" he said.

"No. It can't wait." I could recognize familiar figures moving around on the computer screen behind Oliver's face. With a touch of resentment, I heard the welcome of new guests and the chinking of glasses. I wished I was there—with them.

"We can figure something out when I get back. Or we can speak to Mimi's sister, and see what she has to say," he repeated.

His words were supposed to be reassuring. Oliver was concerned for both of us returning alone, without him, as he saw it. Yet I interpreted his response as unsupportive. It was far from ideal to have this kind of conversation long-distance, but I felt he needed to trust both my professional and personal judgment. I was losing hope of her health turning round. I had been praying, begging God to relieve her from the torment of what she was going through at night. And yet, I felt we had moved beyond the possibility of the Divine working a miracle any time soon. It was, so it seemed, entirely down to us to seek help for her on our own. I pointed out to Oliver that our daughter was not getting any better simply because he was now removed from the immediacy of it all. We were her only hope, and my pain in watching her deteriorate was absolute.

Not wanting to end the conversation in a virtual stand-off, he went on trying to convince me to hang in there. But there was little he could say to persuade me from such a distance, and we hung up with a certain tension between us, one that would last another ten days until his return.

I followed up with Mimi's sister, who lived in Washington DC, via phone calls and emails. She questioned me about Mathilda's history and the results of all the hospital tests, but she was at a loss as to what her symptoms could possibly point toward.

"All I can tell you," she said during my last conversation with her, "is that Mathilda's symptoms indicate something very serious. But I think you already know that, Claire."

No doctor so far away, however experienced, could possibly be expected to work through the complex set of issues that we faced. Mimi's sister was unfamiliar with the National Health Service and baffled by what she saw as my failure to access a diagnosis. I was grateful for her willingness to understand Mathilda's symptoms, and I was sorry that she had lost her own daughter, but I did not have the energy to explain the limitations with which we were working. The health system in the US worked on a completely different model. One I did not understand. With Obamacare still a few years out, socialized health care, as far as I knew, did not exist. I could hardly expect Mimi's sister to help me navigate the differences from across the pond. Besides, all my resources were now focused on getting through the night ahead, handing Liberty and Elliot over to my parents, and having Mathilda successfully admitted once again to Bristol Children's Hospital

12 PSYCHIATRIC THREAT
Mid-May 2010

"Besides, my life is a catastrophe. It is a
catastrophe to be without a voice."

—**E.B.White**
The Trumpet of the Swan

This time, our stay on the observation unit afforded us a single room with our own bathroom. It was the furthest bedroom away from the main station where all the nurses congregated. On the one hand, this gave us privacy, but on the other, if I needed to make a quick run for food or drink, Mathilda would be left alone, with her varying degrees of paralysis and hallucinations. She was not physically on their radar; unless I called a nurse over, leaving her for more than a minute or two would be risky.

A few hours after being re-admitted, we were visited by Rafael, the most junior doctor in the neurology team. I'd met him many times but never unaccompanied by other doctors. Normally, he was left in his colleagues' wake to draw the blood, write up the notes and answer parents' questions. He seemed always at ease, almost casual in his approach to dealing with ill children. This time, he took it upon himself to assess Mathilda. She was awake on the bed, but droopy and vacant.

"She says everything hurts. The nights are the same. Her falling down and ataxia are the same." I went on describing how she had developed hypersensitivity in her feet when walking outside in the back garden; it made her scream, and she needed to wear socks all the time to lessen sensations between her feet and the surfaces she touched. I was afraid her ongoing symptoms were somehow not enough to be taken seriously, and that on the face of it, what really came across was my growing desperation.

"The thing that strikes me about her," Rafael said, "Is that she always looks knackered. She has bags under eyes."

"She is always exhausted. Totally wiped out," I said, sitting across from him, with Mathilda between us on the bed.

"I would even find it bearable if, after a two-hour nap, she woke up refreshed and could do something," I added.

"So when she wakes up, she does not seem refreshed, ever?" he asked.

"No, never. If anything, she is more grumpy and lethargic—the opposite of what you would expect after a long sleep."

"For how long is she awake, once she has woken up?" Rafael continued, whilst preparing to do blood work on her.

"Sometimes minutes. Never more than half an hour," I

said, explaining what a typical day now looked like.

I had almost reached the point of accepting her taking long naps and missing half the day, if only she would wake up energized and ready to go. But she never did.

Walking from the bedroom to the small playroom at the end of the ward, Rafael observed Mathilda from behind. Eventually, she dropped to her knees in front of pile of puzzles, her head lolling up and down, her tongue hanging out and her eyes hooded. She shook her head suddenly, and blinked hard, as if to snap herself into staying awake. We watched her stroke her hand up and down the length of the opposite arm and stretch out the collar of her T-shirt. Anything to avoid nodding off, it seemed.

"One thing I can see when she is walking," he went on, "is that she looks sort of drunk. Other than that, it's a mystery."

Sensing she was not going to last long playing alone, I asked her to clear up before watching her wobble back to the side-room and plunge toward the bed. I lifted her up, and between the doctor and me, we began the ordeal of pinning her down so he could stick the needle in her arm.

"Do you need to take more blood?" I asked, wanting to spare Mathilda another ordeal.

"I know it seems like a lot, but we're gonna need to take her blood twice a day this time."

"Why? Her results are always normal."

"Ah, it's just routine for this type of thing. That way, we can see if anything shows up," he said, tightening the tourniquet and writing her details on tiny white labels.

My dad turned up early the next morning, and eventually he found us in the cardiac unit, where we had been transferred for reasons unknown to me. Being at the hospital stressed him out, and I found his anxiety hard to manage on top of my own. With the exception of an occasional glance at the newspaper, he spent much of that day pacing around Mathilda's bed. There was nothing we could do, there was nothing being done, and not one of our doctors was in sight. The nurse in charge assured me she would find out when our team would visit. In the meantime the lights were dimmed, ready for the night, and Dad left us to help Mum back at the house, where he would at least feel useful. The three sick heart babies around us were all alone. One was just a few days old and covered from head to toes in leads. I was concerned that Mathilda's antics at night would cause a serious disturbance to these infants. Knowing there was very little I could do to really comfort her, I warned our named nurse in advance. She seemed bemused by my prediction, but not in any way perturbed, quite likely because her job was to attend to the heart babies. We were merely occupying a bed. Other than the occasional bleeping of various machines, the rare ringing of the main phone, and my low whispers in Mathilda's ear, the cardiac ward operated in almost total silence.

Oliver called the next morning to inform me of a possible three-day delay with his flight home. Earlier in April, Eyjafjallajokull, an ice-capped volcano, had erupted in southern Iceland. The explosion was so great that the ash ejected from the area was reaching Europe and disrupting air travel. He, like many thousands of people, was literally grounded at various airports around the world because of the potential engine damage from the ash cloud.

I also was stuck with an entirely different problem. With nothing to report other than frequent blood tests, the hospital was becoming less friendly with every visit. We were now, it seemed, being ignored.

Having that sort of conversation with Oliver from a phone at the nurses' station, long distance, surrounded by staff, and in hushed tones, did little to relieve the pressure building between us. Without the privacy to be entirely honest with one another, the conversation ended curtly. I found myself saying, "I guess we'll see you when we see you." He reminded me that I could have waited for him to return before taking Mathilda back in, a comment I interpreted as a pathetic attempt to have the last word and one I responded to by calmly cutting him off. Neither of us had peace.

Both of my parents arrived the next day with Liberty and Elliot, and a bag of things to do and eat. After asking me if we had yet seen anyone, Dad turned towards the nurses' main desk area, unwilling to wait another 12 hours before getting Mathilda looked at. This was our third day, and as yet, Rafael was the only doctor to have stopped by. I hung about the bed with all three children, but could I hear his voice from across the ward, climbing above the peal of crying babies.

"She has been on this unit for over twenty-four hours, and she has not seen a consultant," he said, standing over the ward manager, poised to make a call.

"Do we have the results of the blood test?" Dad asked. "There are no other tests being done, and no one is look-ing at her. My granddaughter is seriously ill, and she needs to see a doctor. Today."

"We did call through to the neurology team yester-day." It was true. They had. "I don't know why they have not been in to see her," she replied, embarrassed.

"I'd like you to call them again. Now." He stayed put until he saw the nurse redialing, and returned only once she had asked for one of the doctors on the neurological team to assess Mathilda, reminding them she was now on the cardiac unit. I allowed myself to relax enough for my appetite to kick in. Realizing I had not eaten in thirty-six hours, I gratefully accepted the food Mum had brought with her.

§

Later that day, Dr. Ellen Dimlock approached us. She was alone. As the intern, she had been present during previous ward rounds and assessments, although I had not seen her during our current stay. She was the one woman on the team and the only doctor who seemed aloof, distant. As she came towards us I stepped forward, hopeful for a new angle on our case. Dr. Dimlock appeared irritated, and took an instant dislike to my father, on account of the earlier phone call, I assumed. I could tell she did not want to be there. But neither Dad nor I expected what came next.

"The team has decided that Mathilda will be referred to CAMHS," she launched in, keeping several steps away from us. "There is nothing more we can do for her." Her tone was cool, official. Dr. Dimlock, it seemed, was only a messenger on this occasion. She wasn't there to assess or discuss or check in with the nurses.

"What department is that?" Truthfully, I had never heard of it.

"CAMHS stands for the Child and Adolescent Mental Health Services. You will both be referred for psychiatric evaluation."

It was then that I understood what she was saying. With a strong sense of disbelief I did my best to keep calm, although any warmth in my voice had long since left.

"Excuse me?"

My Dad let out a small shocked laugh and rubbed his hands through his hair. I thought he might flip out, frustrated as he was with the system and our overall lack of attention that day.

"The psychiatric team will take over her case," she said.

"If you are saying," I replied, clearing my throat, "that this is a case of me just taking Mathilda home and dealing with her behavior, then that is the best news you could give me." I was desperately trying to hold it together because being furious would undermine what little credibility I had left.

"But look at my other children," I insisted, pointing behind me to where the older two were sitting besides Mathilda's bed. Libby looked up from her book alarmed. I wanted to ask her if we seemed like the kind of family who had little else to do other than frequent hospital visits on account of our third child being badly behaved.

"I can do the naughty step, but this is not about that," I countered. "Mathilda is sick, it's a neurological problem, and she needs you."

"There's nothing more we can do for you. It's out of our hands."

With the decision to transfer us to the psychiatric department already made, it was becoming clear to me that our relationship with the pediatric neurology team was almost untenable. Yet I was desperate, and realizing that in the eyes of the team I had already fallen off the tightrope between moderation and madness, there was not much more to lose. I stood there, pleading with Dr. Dimlock to reassess Mathilda, fearing that a psychiatrist would find something in her—the wrong thing. Then, with a label she would probably never shake off, she would sink in the quicksand of medication for the mentally ill. I could see how it would play out, and it terrified me.

"Please," I urged, "the neurology team are the right people looking after Mathilda. I'm sure it's not a psychiatric problem. She's three years old. We can wait until Dr. Jensen has time to see her." My Dad had turned away and walked over to the bed, cursing under his breath and shaking his head.

"There's nothing more we can do," Dr. Dimlock said. "Every time we see her she is either asleep or crying, and almost always non-compliant. The psychiatric team will be able to help shed light on what is going on. We have already referred you both to them." Then, as if speaking the words registered the gravity of what she had implied, my voice raised in disbelief.

"Both of us? Why me? This isn't about me!"

"I'm afraid it might well be, Mrs. Crisp." And with that she turned on her heels and strode purposefully towards the door, digging her hands deep into the pockets of her white coat.

I did not know that there had been a break in the ash cloud covering Iceland. By the time Oliver took a bus from Bristol Airport to the Children's Hospital, we had been relocated, not to the psych unit, but to a renal ward. To this day, I do not know how, or why, it was that we were transferred to another ward to await the blood test results, but what transpired later that Friday evening would alter the trajectory of all our lives.

In the meantime, I had to face the grim prospect of telling Oliver that I'd blown it. Not only was Mathilda still undiagnosed, but both she and I were facing psychiatric evaluation. Standing in the playroom of the renal unit where he had surprised us, he had the air of travel about him with his suitcase in hand, a sharp contrast to my world, which was quickly contracting. Holding Mathilda up to his face and embracing Liberty and Elliot around his middle, he did not create a connection but a distance, tangible and upsetting. I would like to say his presence offered me reassurance, but with another impending discharge, I was now faced with acknowledging that he had been right. I shouldn't have brought her back. It was hard to explain the rationale behind the team's decision without giving credence to Oliver's hesitancy over my resolve to have her re-admitted. In reality, I was too stunned and exhausted for conversation, and we waited there, leaning, for the most part, on the chatter of the children and my parents, although the conversation between my Dad and Oliver was superficial and strained.

The hours dragged on. At one point, the kidney nurse explained that we could go home, pending blood results, and she went off to chase them up. Transferring to the renal unit made no sense, other than being in some sort of holding pattern once more. The promise of home gave us all something to look forward to. But in the waiting, Mathilda grew agitated. She was running low on reserves, becoming highly fractious, and making demands to be back in bed through her own tears of tiredness. It occurred to me we could skip the wait and paperwork and just walk out. A self-discharge would not require a signature, and we could be home in twenty minutes. But fearing the deepening dispute over my potential mental instability, I promised her it would not be long instead, that we all needed to be patient and we would be in the car before dark.

Unannounced and independent of all the other Neurological Consultants, Dr. Siddarth Shah entered the room with the junior half of the crew, including Rafael and Dr. Dim-lock. Up until that moment my expectation was merely to be given the all-clear on the bloods and transferred to the psych team in due course, hopefully as outpatients. Having already become acquainted with all the pediatric neurologists over the past six months both Oliver and I wrongly assumed Dr. Shah was a new permanent consultant. This would explain the four junior doctors' evident lack of confidence as they hovered by the open door in silence. Judging by their demeanor and body language this unplanned visit to Mathilda's room on the renal ward was not how any of them anticipated spending the start to the weekend but for us, it was a last chance to be assessed by an unbiased specialist.

Several minutes later, after scanning every page of Mathilda's notes Dr. Shah raised his eyes and made a statement that swept the room clean of all the staff.

"You are dismissed," he said, handing the large brown medical file across to Rafael.

"Take these with you, they are illegible," he added. Rafael stepped forwards, said nothing and took the notes, picking up several loose papers that had fallen out. There was nothing threatening in Dr. Shah's manner, but his authority was unquestionable. No one challenged him. What he wanted was a clear record of all Mathilda's admissions, symptoms, tests and results, summarized within two hours.

Dr. Shah then turned to us, and we talked at length answering his questions. We tried to wake Mathilda up so he could examine her, but instead she cried, rolled over and once again refused to cooperate. Oliver and I filled in the background of the past few months, united, at least, in our storytelling. I pressed the details of her symptoms and why I was certain they were organic and not psychological in origin fully aware that Oliver also needed to hear why I had made the unilateral decision to bring her in again. There was nothing spectacular going on in that room, only two parents trying to make sense of their daughter's deterioration, and one man's willingness to hear what lay beyond our fears and inside the body of the child on the bed. He listened and observed. We told him what we knew, how she had changed, and the pressure building in us through prolonged sleep deprivation. For him it was a few simple minutes, but for us, it was powerful, profound and subsequently life-changing.

"You need to go home for the weekend. Get out of here," he said. "But I want you to video Mathilda over the next two days. Record what you can and bring it in to me on Monday."

"Back here?" I asked.

"No. Come in to the Clinical Investigations Unit. Eight o'clock," he answered gently. Then he smiled and shook each of our hands before leaving the room.

13 DIAGNOSIS
May 24th, 2010

"Think left and think right and think
low and think high. Oh, the thinks you
can think up if only you try!"

—**Dr. Seuss**
Oh, the Thinks You Can Think

Three days later Mathilda and I returned to Children's Hospital, this time to the Clinical Investigations Unit (CIU), where we waited for the young Dr. Siddarth Shah with our video recording. The tall, dark-headed specialist from India had pursued his medical training in Ahmedabad. He was in the UK, I thought, for good. I didn't realize then that he was merely covering another doctor's leave, and having already spent a month at the Birmigham's children hospital, he was only here for a matter of weeks before returning home. What struck me most in our last meeting was his quietness. He was a man of few words, preferring to listen. Yet there was an unquestionable authority about him, and whilst his manner was gentle and unassuming, it was as though he believed every word we had said. Desperate to avoid the psych department, I had just the tiniest hope that this doctor would take us seriously.

Well into our fifth month of sleepless nights, it was as much as I could do to get to the appointment without falling asleep at the wheel. Feeling so wrecked meant I had absolutely no interest in my appearance, or Mathilda's, for that matter. Still wearing her pajamas and a diaper, she remained slumped and squashed in her baby stroller, in a sleep so deep that she was drooling. I tried to ignore the fact that my clothes were becoming uncomfortably tight and that my unwashed hair had turned from blonde curls to a mussed up bird's nest. Ugly, I thought when I looked in the mirror. Ugly. But for the first time in my life, looking frumpy and disheveled was something I didn't care about. Neither did I worry about scratching our new car on a concrete pillar in the parking lot that morning. What I felt instead was the anticipation of moving forward mixed with a heavy expectation of disappointment. Nevertheless, I could not quite give up on the fact that this consultation held something new and tangible. A hint of hope. The neurology team had opted out, recording in their medical file that they "were not worried about any serious neurological pathology." There was never a moment that I doubted Mathilda's condition was organic, and giving up on her was not an option for me. Somewhere in there was Dr. Shah. Somewhere, somehow, answers were on the horizon.

The previous night was like any other in our house.

Passing with excruciating slowness, each hour was fraught with rising levels of desperation. Mathilda thrashed around her bed, recalling partial nightmares. Seemingly awake yet confused, she dropped off again, constantly muttering gibberish and screaming from the pain in her feet. Hour after hour, she begged for her legs to be taken off. She had bitten her tongue that night, causing it to bleed. Oliver and I alternated shifts, giving her high doses of Tylenol, hot water bottles, food, drinks—anything to try to ease her distress or offer distraction. Many times it would take the two of us in that tiny room to deal with her. We would rub her ankles and hold her close whilst singing quietly, whispering and praying for some sort of miracle. Since his return, Oliver had taken on the majority of her care throughout the night. He was now struggling with exhaustion on top of jet lag. With the weight of the psychiatric referral off our shoulders, it felt good to work as a team again, both on the same page, and pulling in the same direction. But he was still certain nothing new would come from the appointment, and he maintained his pessimism when it came to dealing with any doctor.

When Mathilda had woken that morning in late May, she staggered toward our bedroom across the landing and promptly fell straight back to sleep between us. On the drive to the hospital, she slept through the traffic. She slept through the ride across the subway in the stroller she had outgrown. When I pushed her into the elevator and along the empty hospital corridors, she remained asleep. I was aware that Dr. Shah had only seen her awake for a few minutes the previous Friday. She had been wholly uncooperative then.

As we waited in the abandoned reception area, an episode of the children's TV show, *Charlie and Lola* blared at us from a large flat screen. I began to wonder if anyone would show up. Given the general state of our lives, it was not inconceivable that I could get the wrong location or time of the appointment. The clinic room was adorned with a paradoxical mix of children's storybooks and parental advice leaflets on bedwetting and picky eating. If only. Mathilda's incontinence and peculiar feeding habits were the absolute least of our worries; I refused to read the various brochures. I wished she would just wake up, refreshed. I wanted to hear her chattiness, see her glassy-blue eyes light up, answer her many questions. It seemed so long since I had seen that little girl. I missed her more than ever.

It was difficult to understand how this new doctor could assess Mathilda if she was asleep again. The only thing he had to go on was my reporting of the past few months and the videos in my purse. Yet I also feared her waking up and falling apart, causing Dr. Shah to put the seal of approval on our psychiatric referral. Not really knowing what to do, I decided to leave her as she was in the stroller and play the appointment by ear.

Eventually, I heard our name called. I walked forward, surprised to find that he was already working in the clinic to our right. The room was empty, apart from Mathilda's bulky medical file on the desk, two chairs and a monitor with multiple leads extending to the socket. Several of the walls were glass, and the view of the bustling city was a momentary pleasant distraction. I was glad to find him alone, and wondered how he had handled our case with the team.

"I like a challenge," he said, pointing to the chair beside him. "It's one of the reasons I pursued pediatric neurology. You get to become a sort of 'clinical detective.'" Not quite sure how to respond, I merely nodded in agreement.

"Where I come from, there's not much by way of local resources. Securing a diagnosis is down to the doctor figuring things out." Sitting there, he asked me to walk him through the past six months in detail once again. When had she become so sleepy? Did she hallucinate? Were her siblings fit and healthy? What was a typical night like? How long could she maintain wakefulness in the day? Describe the times she has collapsed.

I simply talked, this time without crying because there was a confidence in him I trusted. He wasn't about to dismiss her symptoms or write the two of us off. My answers came out thick and fast, and I stressed the fact that whatever it was that was wrong with her, she needed 24-hour care.

Without sounding like I was exaggerating, it was hard to communicate how little sleep she was getting and the impact this had on almost every aspect of her life. I was aware of this, but every word that came out of my mouth was the truth. As I articulated a typical twenty-four hour period with the bizarre plethora of symptoms, her distinct change in personality, and all of us becoming virtually housebound, it was possible that Dr. Shah would think I was losing perspective, as many people did. But never had one doctor listened for so long.

One of the recordings we'd taken that balmy weekend had captured Mathilda attempting to play in the back garden whilst eating a grape. She appeared to be asleep and standing up whilst chewing, until her knees gave way, jerking her awake as she staggered off towards the trampoline. Her wobbling gait was remarkable.

"We call this ataxia. It is very clear," Dr. Shah said.

"Yes. Right." I did not like to admit that I understood this, but I knew better than to offer up something that would only be an unhelpful distraction. For the first time in a long while, I began to feel hopeful that we were being taken seriously. This man's questioning was linear and relevant, and his manner gentle. He had the winning combination of being ultra-sharp, assertive and discerning on one hand, and sweet-natured, polite and warm on the other.

In the next video, Mathilda was standing beside the bathtub watching Elliot play in the water. She was trying to get in herself, and was only half dressed. Something Elliot said made her laugh, and grabbing the bath panel as her knees buckled did not prevent the collapse that followed. Down she went. Two other films revealed the extent of her sleeping throughout any given twenty-four-hour period, one three hours into a daytime nap on the sofa with the vacuum cleaner running full blast beside her head. The other at night, and although dark, Mathilda could be heard crying and thrashing around in her bed at 1 a.m. Oliver followed me into the room with the camera, where I whispered, "Mathilda, you really can't keep waking up like this. It is not going to work." You could just barely make out the two of us trying to comfort her through her disorientation and obvious fear. We appeared to be fumbling around in the darkness, failing to reason with a disturbed child. Clearly, it did not compare with the normal waking of a young child, even one with something like a high fever. Both of us were operating well outside of the normal parameters of parenting, fully aware of being out of our depth.

Looking back on those tapes now leaves me feeling not only like an idiot, but also a bad mother. There were times when we both addressed her as a child who was "playing up," who could pull it together if she so desired. To think that night after dismal night we would attempt to coax Mathilda into sustained sleep by reasoning with her was ironic. In the presence of any medic, I insisted that there was something desperately wrong. At home, I pulled every parenting trick out of the hat in the vain hope that one day she might just "snap out of it." We didn't know what else to do. Sometimes, during those first few seconds of waking each morning before my thoughts had oriented themselves, for a few precious moments, I forgot Mathilda's suffering and the pressures that awaited me each day. They were simple minutes of complete happiness before I was jarred back into our reality. More than once I wanted to believe that she would bounce into our room, totally restored to full health, that this nightmare was over and by some miracle, Mathilda was well.

I deeply regret every foolish word I uttered that could have made Mathilda feel "in control" of her symptoms in some way. She was so young. What well did I think she could draw from? Perhaps we could deal with her on an emotional level (even that was incredibly challenging), but understanding her physical symptoms had stumped everyone—until now.

The two of us talked a little more whilst he studied the films again and Mathilda carried on sleeping, unawares. I was beginning to doubt Dr. Shah would perform any kind of meaningful assessment; he seemed uninterested in her waking up and engaging with her. Finally, and without a trace of hesitation or doubt, he looked up and said, "I have never seen this condition in someone under the age of seventeen, but I think I know what it is. She has narcolepsy."

Stunned at the suddenness and certainty of his diagnosis, I frantically tried to grasp what he was saying. arcolepsy. I was not sure of its magnitude or significance, but its gravity clung to me, as if I now owned it. The rational part of mind took over, and I tried hard to focus on the other things he said.

"If we do the blood work today," he said, "and test Mathilda for carrying the genetic marker responsible for narcolepsy, I can confirm her diagnosis by the end of the week." It did not seem real to me. How was it suddenly so easy?

"What does it mean? What is the prognosis?" I begged.

"Narcolepsy is not life threatening, and neither will it shorten her life. But you need to know there is no cure. She is very young." Dr. Shah handed me the videotape.

"Will she improve at all?" I asked. "It is so hard right now. How will she get through this?" I was looking directly at him, scanning his face for more information. He had an answer for her problem. But I wanted *all* the answers for *all* my questions because finally it had a name. I knew that once we left that office, we would be alone again.

"As I said, I have not seen it in a child of her age," he replied. "There is treatment, drug therapy, but I would need to look into it."

My mind immediately cast back to an early Friday evening in April when Dr. Jones, who, at six-foot-something, appeared more frightening than funny to her, tickled Mathilda. He had been sure that we were certainly not dealing with narcolepsy on account of the fact that she hadn't fallen down when he tickled her. "Cataplexy," he said, "is part of narcolepsy, and if she had that, she would not still be standing up. When people with cataplexy feel happy, they collapse." We believed him. The "quick tickle" was a test for a life-long, serious neurological condition. Mathilda had failed that test on account of being afraid of him, not amused by him. It was confusing.

"So why can't she sleep at night, and yet constantly falls asleep all day?" I questioned. Mathilda started to wake and simultaneously cry. I felt my stress levels accelerate as I unbuckled her and pulled her onto my lap.

"Narcolepsy is an autoimmune illness that targets the sleep center in the brain, specifically the hypothalamus. She has lost the ability to sleep normally," he replied whilst writing up her notes. "Cataplexy is the sudden loss of muscle tone when she experiences emotion," he went on. "She has that, too, when her knees buckle or she falls down. It is because she is happy. Cataplexy is a component of narcolepsy.

It's a giveaway, one of the hallmarks."

I had no idea what he was talking about, but I was now faced with trying to wrestle a fractious child towards the lab area where two technicians were preparing to draw her blood. "No! Mummy, no!" Already Mathilda was crying. Too weak to walk, I carried her into the lab room and tried to offer her some comfort. With the word narcolepsy constantly coming back to me, it was hard to focus on the task ahead.

"The nurse lady needs to take your blood so we can all find out what is making you feel so bad," I said. "One more blood test, then we can go home."

The conversation with Dr. Shah was over for now as Mathilda continued her protests. She knew what was happening and did her best to prevent it. Mercifully, the phlebotomists worked quickly, and between the two of us, we kept her arm still whilst she writhed away from the needle. I wished then and there that I could have been the one to offer up my arm. Every time I insisted she comply with a procedure that frightened and hurt her, every time I gripped her firmly and held her still, she battled against me. She felt she lost because I was physically stronger. But the reality was, bit by bit, I also lost a part of her when I became the one to inflict pain and fear. She was now seeing me as she did all medical staff—the enemy.

The weight of the word narcolepsy began to sink in,

along with unsettling questions about her future and what that would look like now. I clung on to Dr. Shah's reassurance that we were not going to lose her altogether. That she was not going to carry on deteriorating and die. This single fact alone gave me the strength I needed to wait several days for his call as our appointment came to a close. With the test tubes of blood that would confirm her diagnosis, I held Mathilda for a while before setting her back down in the stroller and putting her jacket on, careful to avoid moving the arm. Together, she and I turned from the Clinical Investigations Unit, and from the doctor who had single-handedly redirected the course of our lives, but whom we would never see again. I stroked her hair back from her face and watched her fall asleep before we entered the elevator, back down to the congested streets of Bristol.

Alone with my daughter, her sleep disorder, and a conflicting sense of loss and relief, I took a long breath and blocked out the city, impassive and indifferent. Leaning on the stroller allowed me to put one foot in front of the other and push her toward the car, past the office buildings and the homeless in the subway, always asking for the same things. I was acutely aware of the significance of that morning, but had no real notion of what lay ahead for Mathilda, or any of us. For now, the struggle to prove that our young daughter was sick and that we were not mentally ill was over, at last.

14 NEVER A NORMAL TOMORROW
Late May 2010

"It's no use to go back to yestday.
I was a different person then."

—Lewis Carroll
Alice In Wonderland

I knew Dr. Shah's diagnosis was a provisional one, that he would confirm narcolepsy as the culprit as soon as the blood results were in. Once home, I found Oliver typing in the far corner of the kitchen, sitting on an old rocking chair we had picked up in a second-hand shop in London after our honeymoon seventeen years ago. He turned round, fixing me with an expectant look in his eyes. I took a breath before telling him that Mathilda was asleep in the car and about the morning with Dr. Shah. He was seated at just the right level to hold me around my waist, and pulling me in close, he turned my face to his as the word *narcolepsy* impressed itself deeper and deeper into my mind. I said it wouldn't be confirmed until later in the week when Mathilda's blood test revealed whether or not she carried the HLA-DQB1 genetic marker for narcolepsy. But we both knew it then. The scales had been scraped away from our eyes.

We cried, first with relief and the realization that we finally had a name for it. Then we let the diagnosis that was stealing our child settle in our minds before moving toward a greater understanding of what the condition meant. In truth, we didn't know, and with my pathology books long since packed away in the attic, we turned to Oliver's laptop and googled *narcolepsy*.

Working our way through various websites, we quickly absorbed the basic facts—that narcolepsy is a life-long brain disorder caused by a failure of the hypocretin system (the chemicals responsible for regulating our sleep/wake cycles) giving rise to an inability to sleep normally. Seventy thousand neurons in the sleep center of her hypothalamus no longer existed. Gone, destroyed, never to be recovered. I wondered if the cellular demolition that had been going on over the past six months was what Mathilda meant when she said she was *breaking to pieces*. Was it one neuron at a time? Or did the whole lot blow at once? Was it possible that, on some level, she was cognizant of the destruction damaging the chambers of her brain?

We learned that instead of achieving restful Non-Rapid Eye Movement (NREM) sleep, people with narcolepsy oscillate in and out of NREM sleep and experience hallucinations. These intense nightmares not only have visual components, but auditory and tactile elements as well, often combined with vivid technicolor experiences where scale is distorted and disproportionate. Since the narcoleptic sleep pattern is so fragmented, hallucinating goes on throughout the night, with hypnogogic hallucinations occurring just as you fall asleep, and hypnopompic hallucinations arising as you wake. Both are terrifyingly realistic.

I now understood Mathilda's bullfrog dream. It wasn't just that she saw the animal occupying the space between her belly and the ceiling. She felt it, smelled it and touched it. Or rather it touched her. In Mathilda's mind, the larger-than-life bouncing bullfrog was more real to her than we were that night.

Not entering the crucial NREM stage of sleep, the deep sleep where the body repairs itself at cellular level, Mathilda was denied ever waking up restored. She was never rested. The uncontrollable and overwhelming urge to sleep on and off all day was a symptom of Excessive Daytime Sleepiness (EDS). She would nap, but not feel refreshed afterwards. Mathilda's irresistible shutting down giving rise to irritability, poor memory, concentration and withdrawal suddenly all made sense to me. Since Good Friday, Mathilda had been sleepy all day, every day. Some naps were hours long, and micro-naps could be seconds, but the time she spent sleeping was time she lost doing other things—interacting, learning, living.

In the end, cataplexy clinched the diagnosis for Dr. Shah. Derived from the Greek word, *kata*, meaning down, and *plexis*, meaning stroke, Mathilda clearly displayed the symptoms of cataplexy in the videos I had given him. They showed Mathilda losing the strength in her legs when she moved towards something fun, like a trampoline. She could not get there. Her knees would give out halfway across the lawn, and she would fold down more often than not, until she was out cold. I taught the older two to talk her through it, and reassure her that any minute she would wake up. If I wasn't right there, Liberty would do the talking, and Elliot would come and get me. Not more than a minute or so later, Mathilda would come round. What Dr. Shah had identified on the video was a sudden loss of muscle tone, from tongue thrusting to a full collapse in response to an emotion such as anger, surprise, shame or fear. People with narcolepsy *and* cataplexy have their own triggers and remain fully conscious during the attack. Knowing this confirmed that Mathilda could hear us, even when she looked unconscious. Her trigger, it seemed, was happiness. Anything that delighted her would elicit a cataplectic episode. The greater the pleasure, the greater the loss of muscle control. Being three years old, that meant almost any game, the anticipation, or even the idea of one. The only way she could avoid momentary paralysis was not to experience joy.

There was more. Most of the literature and information referenced adults only. We scoured sources for children with the condition, but there was almost nothing, other than the common agreement that the onset of narcolepsy typically strikes between the ages of 15 and 35. There were scientific studies on the consequences of narcolepsy, ranging from psychological, socio-economic, and the extent to which the condition impacted every area of their existence, even their sexual lives. But where were the children with narcolepsy? Was there treatment? Was there something that would control her symptoms? I took it all in, trying to grasp the fact that whilst narcolepsy wouldn't shorten her life, it might ruin it.

"It says there's another symptom called sleep paralysis. She might be waking up fully conscious but not be able to move," I said, lifting my voice. I had not noticed that, at some point during the online search for information, Oliver had stood up and left the room.

"Apparently, people with narcolepsy feel as though their body is frozen as they wake up, often with a sense of choking or the feeling that they are being touched. And they are unable to move or speak. How do we know if she experiences this too?" I asked, my words tumbling out and settling across the empty room like a pall.

There was crying coming from the driveway where I had parked the car. Oliver carried Mathilda in through the hall and laid down with her on the sofa in the lounge. I leaned momentarily in the doorway, watching him stroke her hair, then run his hand over his face before covering her with a blanket. Whilst I wanted to know more, he couldn't take any more.

Everything I discovered rang with permanency. A tiny but significant part of her brain no longer existed, and with that realization went the thin shroud of hope with which I had cloaked myself. There was never going to be a normal tomorrow. Mathilda was not going to get better. And with the exception of calling our families, we spent the afternoon in sinking silence.

15 XYREM
June 2010

> "Sometimes it seemed to him that his life was
> delicate as a dandelion. One little puff from
> any direction, and it was blown to bits."
>
> —**Katherine Paterson**
> ***Bridge to Terabithia***

One thing I started to do was consciously label Mathilda's symptoms. Even without understanding why, knowing what was happening to her drove out many of my fears over her declining health. We had a name for everything that was happening to her, and that, in its own way, gave me a remote sense of control. All remaining anxiety rested on her being treated and our ability to cope with life as around-the-clock caregivers. When her head dropped into her breakfast, flipping the cereal bowl and splashing milk over her hair because Elliot cracked a knock-knock joke, I silently registered *cataplexy*. Amusement was the trigger. The constant sleep disturbance stretching through the small hours was no longer exaggerated night terrors that I tried to coax her out of, but full-blown hallucinations punctuating REM. I understood that she couldn't achieve sustained NREM sleep, and why, in turn, she spent most of the day in a weakened and irritable state. Narcolepsy was taking its place in our family, like an odious relative who had turned up unannounced and told us he was staying for good—uninvited and unwanted.

Two days after our meeting with Dr. Shah in the clinical investigations unit, he rang me at home.

"Mathilda has the genetic marker HLA-DBQ1 for narcolepsy," he said, getting straight to the point. "I think when we add up all her symptoms, the clinical picture is clear. We could do a lumbar puncture to measure hypocretin levels in the spinal fluid, which is typically low in people with narcolepsy but in her case, I don't think it's necessary. She's already been through a lot, and her cataplexy is striking."

I wasn't surprised by the blood test results, and having surfed the internet, exhaustedly, I had questions only a doctor could answer. They were flying around in my head.

"What caused her to have narcolepsy and cataplexy? Why does she have it?" I asked, turning towards the older children and signaling them to leave the room.

"Since narcolepsy is an autoimmune illness, in addition to carrying the gene, there's an environmental trigger. Like flu, strep throat…something like that. Did she have any kind of infection before her symptoms started?"

"No, not that I recall. She was completely healthy," I answered, casting my mind back over the months to the last time one of the kids had a cold, an infection or a fever. "There's been nothing significant," I said. "As you know,

Mathilda had laryngo-malacia which she grew out of by two. We've taken her to Princeton, and since we've been back, she's been well the whole time."

"It may be difficult to say what her trigger was, but I do know she is exceptionally young, and that might make treating her a challenge." I sensed Dr. Shah's clipped answers and the moving voices in the background, indications that he needed to hang up. My remaining questions would have to wait.

Other than that conversation, we had no contact with any of the doctors until arriving at the outpatient clinic three weeks later. I had set off excited to see Dr. Shah again and talk about treatment options. Maybe Mathilda would be alert enough to meet him, finally. Much of our online research indicated that there were pharmacological options of varying effectiveness. Daytime stimulants and anti-depressants would keep her awake and control the cataplexy, and a more controversial medication was available for the nights—Sodium Oxybate. Known by its brand name, Xyrem, it was a relatively new drug, one that restored quality of life by allowing deep sleep at night for several hours at a time. It hit EDS on the head, condensing the constant unavoidable sleepiness into several isolated naps a day. On Xyrem, a person with narcolepsy would have the opportunity to live something that resembled a near-normal life. For Mathilda, who had barely begun childhood, I clung to the possibility that it could make all the difference.

But Xyrem wasn't without side effects, and some were serious. Nor was its use limited to the treatment of narcolepsy. Referred to in the bodybuilding world as GHB (Gamma Hydroxybutyrate), it is the ideal supplement in the quest for larger, leaner muscles—the perfect body. On the partying scene and in clubs, it's known to most as the date-rape drug, notoriously abused and with an astronomical street value. Shocking as it was to consider this treatment as an option, the information I gathered suggested Sodium Oxybate was the best option out there. With medication foremost in my mind, Mathilda and I returned to the pediatric outpatients' department at Bristol Children's Hospital mid-June.

After the usual checking in, I sat in a row of chairs beside the giant fish tank, ready to distract Mathilda should she stir. I had become adept at cramming tidbits of information into minutes of wakefulness in the hope that she might retain something useful from the day that was otherwise lost to her. On this occasion, Dr. Jensen appeared at the entrance of the noisy waiting room before I realized he was calling out Mathilda's name.

"Where's Dr. Shah?" I asked, following him to the office and failing to hide my incredulity.

"He left." I was stunned. Dr. Shah had arranged this

appointment. There had been no talk of handing Mathilda back over to the neurology team. I sat down on the other side of a desk that separated us, burning with frustration.

"How is she doing?" he said, peering over the rim of his glasses and crinkling the lines of his forehead.

"Where did he go? Is he coming back?" I began to panic, thinking he might pick up where the team left off a few weeks earlier, with the psychiatric referral.

"Dr. Shah was only here for three weeks. I'm not sure what his plans were afterward. It looks like Mathilda might have narcolepsy," he replied, whilst thumbing through her thick medical file.

"You are very fortunate we got to this point so quickly. The average time it takes to diagnose narcolepsy is ten to fifteen years." My mind raced after Dr. Shah, wondering how, or even if, I could find him.

"I think we should administer a Multiple Sleep Latency Test (MSLT), to be absolutely sure," he said. "Without confirmation, it is going to be hard to know how best to treat her. It's less invasive than a lumbar puncture. What do you think?" he said. "We can do it here."

"She needs treatment. She needs to be able to sleep at night and wake up during the day. Isn't the fact that she has the HLA-DQB1 marker and a full house of symptoms enough?" I replied, trying to orientate my thoughts. Mathilda began to stir in the stroller, waking momentarily to readjust her position. I lifted her up into an embrace, praying she would stay quiet so we could keep talking.

"To reach a definitive diagnosis we need to run the MSLT. I'll arrange for this to be done as soon as possible. I think it would be sensible to withhold treatment until we have definitive proof of the diagnosis." I stifled a sigh of disbelief.

"What about Xyrem, Sodium Oxybate? Apparently it helps people with narcolepsy to sleep at night. I can't help thinking that if she could sleep at night, her daytime symptoms would improve."

"I would have to look into it," he countered. "It's a very expensive drug and difficult to get a hold of. With cases like this, we would need to make an application to the board and justify why the National Health Service should spend thousands of pounds when Xyrem isn't proven to help children as young as Mathilda. Then they will argue that for every one Mathilda, the same amount of money could treat, say, five other children who also need specialized medication. But we can try," he finally ended, leaning back in the chair with his hands behind his head.

I was discouraged by what would be an uphill struggle, a battle we might not win, or that would take years to break through. In effect, he was saying that we were not going to get treatment any time soon. Since I understood the NHS to be slow, and with Mathilda's age against her, I believed him.

Either way, I saw each day of her childhood slipping away. Dr. Jensen had exposed me to a reality where there were other children similarly desperate for treatment. If their plight was as hard as ours, then I was torn. Pushing forward with an application for Xyrem would leave us guilty of depriving other families.

"In the meantime, a colleague of mine at Oxford is an expert in sleep disorders, and I would like her opinion," he offered helpfully.

"That sounds good. And Xyrem, can we at least apply for that?" I asked, shelving the ethical dilemma for now.

"And is there anything that will help her pain?" I asked. "Last night she screamed for her legs to be taken off. Massaging her ankles helps but it's not enough. Oliver and I are trying our best, but she's really struggling with it."

"Try giving her the maximum dose of Tylenol. There may be options for the pain later but let's get the sleep test done and have Dr. Abdul in Oxford take a look at her as soon as possible," he replied.

I thanked him for his help, relieved that our mental instability was no longer in question, and that Xyrem was at least part of the conversation. Securing Mathilda back in the stroller, I followed him to the open door and shook his hand before leaving.

§

They conducted the Multiple Sleep Latency Test in the same room as the sleep-deprived EEG—a bare space with a clinical plinth, a desk, and a mobile monitor unit connected to dozens of color-coded electrical leads. The wires were carefully attached to Mathilda's head one by one, each secured by strong glue. She was supposed to take four or five twenty-minute naps, set two hours apart, during which she should have stayed awake. This would allow for accurate data of her brain function, REM and muscle activity to be recorded. But when the technician roused Mathilda to begin the wake time, she was unmanageable beyond consolation, and pleaded with us to be left alone and allowed to sleep.

Despite our best efforts to keep her awake with games and books, instead of the two-hour wake period, the irresistible urge to sleep overpowered her. It was hard to explain to the technician how this was pretty typical, and even harder to enforce the MSLT schedule on her. She just couldn't do it. The seven hours it should have taken extended to ten. Before dusk draped itself over the city, I began to blame the lack of curtains and the absence of a pillow for his failure to obtain the information we needed to be let home.

§

In the few broken hours of sleep I collected each night, my own dreams began to take on a bizarre, almost vision-like quality. One in particular, though I thought little of it at the time, was so real that I wrote it down the next day. I have never been one to keep a journal, but throughout those months I started to carve out a quiet hour in the afternoons when I could sit down and be still. Often I read. Sometimes I listened to choral music, Allegri's *Miserere*, Bach's *Mass in B Minor*, or Beethoven. Other times I meditated on a Bible verse. Still others I sat in front of the window, dazed, staring blankly as neighbors pulled their cars into their driveways and others passed by with their dogs.

The dream I documented in my brown leather notebook featured a perfectly arched bridge. Mathilda was beginning to walk over it, holding onto the wooden rail, stumbling and pausing to find her balance. On the other side sat a large group of children on the grass, all smiling and beaming in the sunlight. It took her a long time to reach the top, and once there she hesitated before letting go of the rail. Beyond the children were beautiful gardens, like Eden. Cascading waterfalls, lakes with Koi fish and exotic plants sparkled in acres of jeweled green grass, as far as the eye could see. Then, beginning her descent, her friends stood and clapped. Some cheered. As the strength returned in her legs, she ran down the other side of the bridge, without so much as wavering, and took her place amongst them on the grass. It was a vision that would return to me so frequently

I began to wonder if the place really existed.

Those moments I spent in quiet reflection kept the despair into which I felt I was submerging from devouring me. For a few minutes each day, I had a tangible sense of centering and control, of the power to slow the pace at which everything was changing. My thirty laps in the pool every morning became physically impossible. I was barely able to educate Liberty and Elliot. By the afternoons, I would feel the need to drown depression in the better part of a bottle of Beaujolais, blocking out the building pressure and bracing myself for the grim hours ahead. Often I was jolted back from the quiet reassurances of scripture, and putting my pen down, I moved over to the crying child slumped before me. She was there, in her own vacant time frame, blurring the boundaries between night and day, moving me beyond exhaustion into a ghostlike sense of reality, redefining all of our lives.

Oliver and I had begun to process the implications of narcolepsy, but our innermost fears settled about her future in different places. His extended into Mathilda's adulthood, dreading the possibility that she would never live independently. *Would she always need someone with her twenty-four hours a day to hold her on the toilet and anticipate every fall? Would we be tied to the home that we shared when she was thirty? Would we give up our plans for traveling through Europe and writing together?* These were questions he voiced only once, but I knew they weighed heavily on him, like a millstone around his neck. For me, the hypnogogic hallucinations and the deadening exhaustion required an effort that left me blinded. Having broken down each day into manageable 15-minute segments, I couldn't see her future, or ours.

Despite our polarized perspectives, Oliver would encourage me to hang in there in the evenings. He never offered pep-talks or glib assurances of everything turning out well, promises he knew he couldn't make. Rather, he reminded me of what our faith meant, that it was real, that we were in this together, and that having each other and the kids would be enough. If I went down, he said, the wheels of our family would come off. I found his belief in me encouraging, but it left me thinking he didn't understand that I was hanging onto the ledge of hope by my fingernails. I couldn't reconcile myself to Mathilda being like this for the rest of her life. In my moments of solitude, I tried praying her out of it. When that didn't work, I begged.

I concealed private thoughts of losing my grip from everyone, even him. Oliver was moving toward a point of acceptance faster than I was, and although I knew I should have been treading the same path, I just couldn't get there. I didn't share the depth of my emotional free falling, the spiritual turmoil, or the many passages I wrote down—evidence of a fragility that I feared might yank him over the edge with me. Together we focused on getting Mathilda treatment. In our minds, that meant Xyrem.

16 THE WIND OF FREEDOM BLOWS
July 2010

"There she paused for a while thinking…but the
temptation was so great she could not conquer it."

—Charles Perrault
Bluebeard

I grew up under the maternal wings of a mother, a grand-mother, and a great-grandmother who hung on long enough for me to produce her very own great-great granddaughter. Great Nan (never Ethel) lived by many matriarchal mottos as though they were some kind of guarantee to life unfolding without creases, if, and only if, you wholeheartedly lived by them—as she did. Most of the time she would remind my sister and me of her recipe for a successful life while leading us to the front door by her cold papery hand, past the bathroom smelling of talc and layers of dried urine, and past the sideboard with its decaying plants and faded photos. I saw most of her sayings as superstitious. *Grow a money plant in your house and you'll be rich.* But some were practical. *Spend half, save half* and *drop'em and wash'em.* This became a family joke since it had something to do with cleaning your underwear. Almost all referred to living economically, right down to her monthly reminders of *"don't mourn me when I'm gone,"* which she told us would be a waste of time. I never owned up to the fact that every indoor plant I grew dropped its leaves (I would never be rich), or that saving on a Physical Therapist's salary in London was unrealistic. But I valued her optimism when the chips were down. Waving us goodbye from the front door, her voice and hands quivering, we would look back and acknowledge her advice in turn.

"Remember girls," she would warble, *"everything happens for a reason."*

Having dropped off the homeschool scene in Bristol for the past six months, very few people knew what was really going on with us. Those that did offered what they could. Wendy, I cried on. Sam, I leaned on, and a few others visited and watched me splutter through conversations about how well Libby and Elliot were holding up. Another homeschool friend, Kate, called to ask me if I wanted to connect with the wife of her husband's cousin in Rome. They had a boy that had something wrong with him, she recalled, something that sounded similar to what Mathilda had.

In what became lengthy email exchanges with a woman my age named Josephine, I discovered that her 12-year old son Stephen had developed narcolepsy after a bout of flu, just before they relocated to Italy several years ago. He was under the care of a sleep specialist there, and was responding to treatment well enough to play on the school cricket team. Xyrem had made all the difference, lifting him off the sofa and into the classroom, where he was thriving. Accessing treatment and specialist care for their son in Rome had been relatively straightforward, despite being internationals. They were not coming back, she said.

Josephine admitted that our situations were different, and she advised me to seek help from Stanford University, a leading center for narcolepsy research in California. Stephen hadn't been accepted into Stanford's treatment program, but given Mathilda's age, we might have better luck. I had never heard of the program until then.

Mali Einen was a name that appeared on one of those email threads. I soon learned that she was the personal assistant and right hand of Professor Mignot, a French scientist and leading researcher in the field of narcolepsy. As a top-tier research university just south of San Francisco, Stanford offers one of the most elite educations in the world. Its student body represents 50 states and 90 different countries, and it has shaped the minds of world leaders, including John F. Kennedy and Condoleezza Rice. In every department, from business to bioengineering, notable alumni have graduated since its foundation in the late 1800s. Today, the Center for Narcolepsy Research, headed by Professor Emmanuel Mignot, makes advances into understanding the mechanisms behind autoimmune disorders across the clinical spectrum. Mali Einen oiled the wheels of the center, bridging the interface between Mignot the scientist and Mignot the pediatric specialist. Mali connected with parents like me, to help children like Mathilda. She was unique in her role and insights, not least because she, too, has narcolepsy.

In early August, just after Mathilda's fourth birthday, we had a Skype meeting with Mali. I was nervous about talking to another person with narcolepsy for the first time, unsure of what I might find, and to what extent the condition defined her. I only knew that speaking to her was the next step, one that I hoped would move us forward, even if incrementally. The rain was drumming down on our lounge windows with a vigor that threatened the internet connection linking us to her small office in Palo Alto, five and a half thousand miles away. Oliver had pedaled home from work early so we could both hear what she might say. After setting the children up with a video upstairs, he leaned into the screen beside me. Then, through the distant crackle on the line, I heard my own voice bounce back, ahead of her cheery American accent.

"Hello. Thanks for taking the time to talk to us," I said, trying to hide my apprehension.

"Oh, no problem. It's a pleasure. Tell me about Mathilda and how you are all doing." Her voice was clear, upbeat.

She looked bright and breezy on the screen. Professional. What had I expected? Someone who slurred her words and dropped in and out of a sentence? Someone who was massively overweight and too tired to brush her hair?

"Well, I'm not sure where to begin," I said, my voice beginning to buckle and my legs trembling with nerves. "She's really struggling with the nights, just getting through them and the hallucinations. Mathilda says things like, 'I want to sleep but my body won't let me.' And she naps on and off all day. She's fallen asleep in the bath, in the pool, at the beach, breathing sand through her nose. It's anywhere and everywhere," I said. "When she's awake, we can't take our eyes off her because of the cataplexy. Sometimes it's just that she rolls her tongue around the inside of her bottom lip, but at other times, she collapses right down to the floor."

"Do you know what she's feeling when she is having a cataplectic attack?" Mali asked calmly.

"No," I said, after thinking about it. "She can't tell me."

"Well, to stave it off, to resist the knee buckling and collapsing, requires the same effort as lifting a truck," she said matter-of-factly. "You keep lifting until it becomes too heavy and there's nothing you can do but go down under it. That's what it is like for an adult. I can imagine it's harder for a three-year-old." I began to cry quietly.

"She's just turned four," I said, as if it would make a difference.

"So from her point of view," she went on, "it's something she will be fighting, but always losing against. It's a tug-of-war she can't win. How many times a day does she have an attack?"

"I honestly don't know. It would be easier if you asked me how many times a day is she cataplexy free. Because if she's not rolling her tongue or stumbling over or totally down, then she's asleep," I replied, not realizing my voice was rising, as if to validate my words. I was afraid Mali wouldn't believe me.

"And the tiredness she feels, it's outside of the normal experience of exhaustion. She will never feel rested, even after a long nap," she added.

"That's one of the things I find so hard. If she had the energy to do something after sleeping all morning then we could plan on things, get out of the house, do stuff," I answered, lifting the laptop to get a clearer line.

"It's always a big adjustment to go from leading a normal life to coping with a chronic illness. Getting a diagnosis like this is a big deal, and Mathilda is exceptionally young. You really are in a unique situation. Don't underestimate the impact this will have on the whole family," Mali said, reaching into a situation that I had barely begun to process. I knew from everything I had read that narcolepsy was life-long, that she would never be free of it. But hearing Mali say it felt like someone was clubbing me over the head, as if to whack it into me. Oliver passed me a box of Kleenex before leaving the room to check on the children. Standing momentarily in the doorway, he signaled for me to calm down and to reign myself in, as though I was embarrassing him. I turned back to the screen and met Mali's eyes.

"We don't know what to do. Mathilda is under a team of pediatric neurologists here in Bristol that we see every few weeks, but we've already been told we are going to have to justify why she needs treatment. I've worked within the National Health Service, and my sense is that getting Xyrem for Mathilda will take years. If she goes without treatment, she'll lose her childhood," I said, moving off screen to wipe my face.

"I will speak to Professor Mignot. Treatment can make all the difference, and if you can get her on Xyrem she will do so much better than she is now. When I started on it in my mid-thirties, it was life changing. She has every right to try it. Frankly, I find it appalling that treatment in England is elusive, although not many specialists will have the experience to treat a child as young as she is. But I am more than happy to advise Mathilda's doctor, so by all means, connect us both through email. In the meantime, can you send me the video footage and a copy of her medical notes?"

"That would be great. Yes. Thank you." My voice returned with relief and gratitude.

I didn't want the conversation to end, to switch Mali's

face off the screen. She was a window into Mathilda's inner world, a place that I hadn't been able to access for eight months. Giving me insight into what narcolepsy felt like meant I might be able to find Mathilda again, even if it was in the dark tunnel of hallucinations and periodic paralysis. I was lifted by Mali's radiance, by how she articulated what was going on inside Mathilda's body. She was holding down a job, a demanding one. She was wide-awake and wearing make-up. Maybe Mathilda would do that one day, and have the coordination to dress and drive herself to work. Maybe we wouldn't always have to hold her on the toilet seat while she fell asleep peeing. Maybe she wouldn't be tortured each night by her hallucinations. For now, by offering to advise our team at the children's hospital, Mali Einen had tied a knot in our rope—thick enough to hold on to.

At the next outpatient appointment, Oliver and I were up-beat, and we informed Dr. Jensen about the opportunity to work with Stanford. I stressed that it was a free service and only required conversations via email. He said he would check his inbox, but in the meantime, Mathilda was to be started on Modafinil, a stimulant that would help keep her awake in the daytime. Widely used as a treatment for nar-colepsy, he was confident that she would respond well to

100mg a day, increasing to 200mg the next month.

He was overworked, I told myself. Contacting Mali was something he would get to by the end of the week.

"Have you received the appointment to see Dr. Abdul in Oxford yet?" he asked us.

"No. Not yet," I answered, feeling pressured on the spot, as though it was something we hadn't taken care of.

"The results of the Multiple Sleep Latency test were unhelpful, verifying that there is no electrophysiological evidence of hypersomnolence or REM intrusions to suggest narcolepsy." Dr. Jensen moved the piece of paper with the results scribbled towards me. "This is going to make a case for Xyrem very hard." I looked down, trying to fathom why the ten-hour test used as a definitive diagnosis for narcolepsy had come back negative.

"We'll have to repeat it. I don't doubt she has narcolepsy, but we need proof, as it were," he said, filing the paper away and jotting down notes.

"My concern with giving Mathilda a stimulant is that she is not sleeping at night," Oliver said. "It seems counterintuitive to stimulate wakefulness in the day when she's utterly knackered. Won't it be harder for her to cope?"

"Giving her a stimulant to stay awake in the day might force her to sleep at night," Dr. Jensen replied, pushing his chair back and standing.

"I can't see the logic in that when we know that narcolepsy is an autoimmune condition," Oliver said. "How will it force her to sleep when her sleep center doesn't produce the chemicals to sustain NREM sleep?"

"No one knows how she will respond to any treatment. We are all on new territory. Modafinil is an effective stimulant. I think you will see an improvement in her," he said with finality.

I forced myself to stay positive, to remain optimistic about her improving, and to be patient.

Within a week, I spoke to Mali again. Professor Mignot was eager to have samples of Mathilda's blood. Arrangements could be made for a box of test tubes to be sent via Federal Express to our house, if we were in agreement. She was surprised that Dr. Jensen had not responded to her emails and suggested I mention it again the next time we met with him. I gave her specific information about Mathilda and a detailed timeline of the onset of her symptoms and hospital admissions.

It would take some time, but once her blood was tested in Stanford's laboratory, they would confirm that Mathilda was the youngest patient they had ever come across. Being the foremost center for narcolepsy research in the world meant she was the youngest diagnosed person with narcolepsy on record at the time—a fact that made our situation even more complex and isolating.

It never occurred to me that we wouldn't be able to find

someone to draw Mathilda's blood; she had already been pinned down and bled numerous times. However, she was no longer an inpatient, and local offices had a policy restricting the phlebotomist to draw only adult blood. We were left with the box of test tubes on our own.

I called every private hospital in the Southwest. Not one would accept a request for blood work that came from overseas, that wasn't authorized by a British specialist. I begged a doctor who was a friend to do it on the down low, in the kitchen at his house if necessary. When he said it would compromise his professionalism, I dragged her back to Dr. Bledsoe. Beyond any care that I was quietly going crazy, I took the unopened cardboard box of test tubes and Mathilda to his office at Fishponds Family Practice. I explained that Stanford was willing to advise us all on how to treat her. We needed their expertise going forward, but the tradeoff was a sample of Mathilda's blood. Dr. Beldsoe, like all the others, refused for the same reason. They just weren't authorized, and there were no other options. And so it went on for the next couple of months with calls and appointments, and with Oliver and I toying with the idea of getting hold of a needle and figuring it ourselves. We got nowhere.

It was true that Modafinil had made Mathilda more alert in the late afternoons, but it came at a price. She could now sustain a three-hour wake period, but through most it, she was aggressive, alternating between crying fits and bouts of anger. After two weeks at the higher dose, the violent mood swings became so intolerable that we pulled her down to a 100mg a day. We decided to approach our local Member of Parliament in order to speed up the application for Xyrem. If drawing blood was this hard, and with the inconclusive sleep test results, how realistic was it that we had a case for treatment? The letter outlining our concerns over Mathilda's health and our quest for Xyrem eventually reached the Chief Executive of Bristol Children's Hospital, who passed it down to Dr. Jensen.

His written response stated that Mathilda only had a provisional diagnosis. She was, in fact, already receiving treatment under his team at the hospital. Modafinil, an appropriate medication, was proving to be effective. On the other hand, Xyrem, should we ever receive funding, was not tried or tested in young children. In order to be certain of the efficacy of Xyrem, the letter read, he would be seeking national and international advice, as well as a second opinion from Oxford. "If she does indeed have narcolepsy," he stated, "she will be one of the youngest cases ever recorded." No one, he pointed out, had ever treated a Narcoleptic as young as Mathilda, not even Stanford.

That fall, our family took a break from the vicissitudes of

our lives. We journeyed to Center Parcs in Somerset, an hour's drive from Bristol. My parents, together with my sister Amanda, her husband James, and their son Lucas were waiting to celebrate my fortieth birthday. They had organized for us to stay in a woodland lodge next to theirs, and just a few yards away from the main attraction—a pool complex with slides and water rapids. Over the weekend, I watched my eighteen-month-old nephew walk a hundred yards to the pool without falling down. He stayed awake after two hours of swimming. I loved his boundless energy and constant chatting. Realizing Mathilda was not as functional as a toddler reminded us of how far away she had drifted since the beginning of the year. We were alone in our world, where I had only older children to compare her with, and an almost housebound routine that allowed us to get through a twenty-four hour period. I had begun to lose touch with how far she had slipped. It took concentrated effort to remember the girl she used to be.

My mum and sister had gone all out on throwing me a birthday party. The two of them spent the day decorating their lodge with banners and balloons, and the table was laden with gifts and cards with messages of love. I did my best to take part in the spirit of celebrating turning forty, but I was distracted by what I thought would be our last conversation with Mali later that same evening. Oliver had arranged another Skype meeting, which, because of the time difference and Mali's schedule, meant we needed to cut the party short and set up the internet connection next door.

Both of us were embarrassed by the box of empty vials still sitting on top of our freezer back in Bristol and the unreturned emails from Dr. Jensen. In previous exchanges with Mali, I had explained the boundaries of the National Health Service and why it was proving impossible to get Mathilda's blood drawn. With the standard practice of blood tests on children in the US, it looked as though we were deliberately dragging our feet. Oliver led the conversation that evening, reassuring her that we would soon find a way to fill and return the vials, although neither of us knew how, having already exhausted every avenue we could think of. As the brief conversation drew to a close, I knew that if the box from Stanford remained empty, we could wave goodbye to their help. The thought was too terrible to accept.

One night, about a week later I found myself sitting in Dr. Bledsoe's office. It wasn't late, but the darkness of the evening had crept into the building, stilling the waiting room and offices that led off from the corridor. There were no children running around, no elderly folk coughing, no receptionists at the front desk. The only sounds came from the low drone of a vacuum cleaner and the hum of street lighting beyond the window.

"There's no shame in it. Lots of people need a little prop

now and then to get through a rough patch. Not to mention hitting the big four-zero," Dr. Bledsoe said, winking.

"I've never been on anti-depressants." I replied, looking down at the floor.

"We could start you on a low dose, and see how you do. You might need a little increase along the way but perhaps by next summer, you'll be in a different place."

"How will it be different?" I asked him. "And can either of us possibly tell whether I am depressed or sleep deprived? I'm so tired. It's as though I am walking around in a dense fog all the time, fighting off a virus of some kind." It was unlike me to be confrontational, but I felt weak, like every word was draining out of me.

"I see from your notes that you spent a day this week at the ER. How's your finger doing?" he asked warmly.

"It's fine. I ran it under the sewing machine making a costume for Elliot. They pulled the needle out of the bone. It's no big deal," I said, not wanting to dwell on it. The truth was, I had fallen asleep just as my right hand slipped under the foot of the sewing machine, breaking the needle and leaving my index finger trapped in the material. Unable to yank it out ourselves meant another trip to hospital. This time Liberty came with me and watched while a nurse used a small pair of pliers to extract the needle and fabric from my finger before bandaging the whole hand.

"At the partner's meeting today, we discussed Mathilda's

case again. I am sorry, but we really don't know how to help other than medicating you until things get easier," he said with sympathy.

"There is something you can do." I said slowly. "I know I asked this last time I was here…could you please take Mathilda's blood so it can be sent to Stanford? I am at a loss as to why nobody can do this one simple thing. It's just *one* small thing." He stared at me thoughtfully. There was a silence between us that I would normally have filled, but I let my words carry their weight.

"I know a phlebotomist at the Clinical Investigations Unit and could call in a favor. Could you get her there early, before it opens?" he offered.

"Yes. Of course," I said, blinking away the tears that had filled my eyes. I looked at him, then down at the requests he was writing out: a six-month supply of Prozac, and the name of someone who would meet us first thing in the morning.

Although the appointment with Dr. Bledsoe was brief, a seemingly insignificant exchange between two people, it was a pivotal moment. In the quietness of that room, and after months of presenting Mathilda to every doctor in the practice, I held in my hand a nine-digit number—a hinge on which all our lives would turn.

As soon as I arrived home, I lifted the box from Stanford down from the freezer and opened it. Inside were eight labeled glass vials, and a stack of papers that needed our signatures. The first page was a letter outlining how Mathilda's blood would be used for research purposes. The sheet was headed with Stanford's red insignia, a single fir tree set amongst mountains and encircled by five words. *Die Luft der Freiheit Weht.*

Standing there, staring into the glass vials, I reached back to the person I had once been, who had helped rehabilitate hundreds of patients from illnesses and surgeries in hospitals, homes and clinics. It wasn't only that I was depressed or exhausted, but that I was alone in failing my own child by not giving her what I had managed to do for countless others. My thoughts turned to our children upstairs. Liberty and Elliot asleep, and Mathilda without the seventy thousand neurons she needed. Where were they? How would I find them and give them back to her? Would I ever stop hearing the echo of my voice every time I looked at her? *I can't help you. I can't help you. I can't help you.* It was these same words that I was too afraid to tell my Grandmother, on whose deathbed even my hands couldn't bring life into. My mind hurled back over the years, clutching to the advice my parents had instilled in me whenever a situation seemed impossible—*never give up.* I heard my Great Nan's words—*everything happens for a reason.* I reflected on Oliver's confidence in me, that I would in time not curse the darkness but light a candle in it. We had no way of knowing whether Mathilda, the youngest child with narcolepsy in the world, would ever be restored, but with robotic precision, I began to read the dozens of pages outlining the details of the research program at Stanford led by Professor Mignot.

And with pen in hand, I signed the last few documents, pausing at the top of the page to retrieve fragments of German I had learnt in school.

Die Luft der Freiheit Weh. The Wind of Freedom Blows.

17 THE CITY OF DREAMING SPIRES
October 11th, 2010

"Don't spend your time looking for something
you want but cannot be found."

—Rudyard Kipling
The Jungle Book

Oliver and I knew Oxford well. For him, it meant presenting academic papers at the prestigious Oriel and Regent's Park College and attending conferences at Lady Margaret Hall. I, too, had taken the children on walking tours around the various colleges, such as Trinity and Balliol, and spotted the sites where Harry Potter was filmed, like the dining room at Christchurch. It was real-life Hogwarts for them, seeing the mahogany dark walls lined with imposing portraits of great thinkers and long benches lit by low amber lamps that stretched all the way to the Dons dining at high table. We lingered there in those places, enjoying the ambience and the air, pregnant with energy and ideas emerging from hundreds of years of lectures, discussions and conversations. On another visit, we saw a Stradivarius at the Ashmoleum Museum, amongst other exhibits, before popping our heads into The Eagle and Child. It was here in this simple pub that Tolkien had met with C.S. Lewis and other formidable writers who had transformed the landscape of British literature decades before. After that, I took the children to the banks of the Thames. There we watched free-spirited youths fall in love, drifting toward pubs and evening tutorials on a cool afternoon as the sun peaked before descending behind the quadrants and walled gardens.

Oxford's reputable excellence extended to its hospitals, including the Children's Unit, where medical specialists, like academics, are thought to be at the top of their game. Although we had waited months for our appointment for Mathilda to come through, it felt good to be back in a place that was familiar, a place we trusted. The magic of those early encounters extended to the black and white print on the documents we now took with us to an entirely different place—the John Radcliffe Hospital.

For this hospital visit, the three of us drove seventy miles from Bristol, via Swindon, along the serpentine A420, where a deep fog hovered above the ground. It lifted slowly, revealing rambling hedgerows and the intense green of unfurling hills further off. Shortly after arriving at Seacourt Park and Ride, a desolate space on the outskirts of the city, devoid of the ancient architecture associated with the home of the oldest university in the English-speaking world, we found ourselves on a single-decker bus, weaving our way toward the hospital. It should have been a ten-minute drive as the crow flies, but the streets were gridlocked that morning, as much as any other, with cyclists, pedestrians and vast quantities of buses circling the city.

Seeing the young students peddling about with backpacks brimming with books, I wondered if Mathilda would ever have the coordination and energy required to do the same. Would she ever ride a bike? Would she re-emerge in time to delight in reading the childhood classics that awaited her on our bookshelves? Would she make her own plans beyond getting off the couch and out the front door? Plans that would bring her somewhere like this? I desperately wanted that for her, even if that came with typical teenage rebellion. I couldn't reconcile the vivacious young adults with their potential and futures wide with opportunity to the child I was holding on the bus. A girl that I could not wake up.

The pediatric center of the Radcliffe was nestled within a sprawling residential neighborhood. Its gray cement exterior was uninspiring, and it looked better suited to a business park than to the leafy suburbs in which it was situated. Inside it was bright, airy, and considerably more welcoming with elevated glass ceilings and tiny tiled handprints of patients lining wall after wall. The main entrance area was deserted, with the exception of one or two chatty porters pushing older children in wheelchairs. I pulled out the paperwork to check we had the right time and to confirm where we would find our expert.

Unaware of the journey we had made across the country that morning, Mathilda awoke, and she began to complain about being in a new hospital.

"I bet there'll be some toys for you to play with," Oliver said as we mounted the escalator.

"I don't want them to have my blood anymore. And no more men doctors."

"Agreed. It's just going to be us talking today. No blood work or tests, and you won't have to stay here overnight," he added.

"We're here so that we can figure how to get you better," I chimed in as we pushed her into a waiting area and headed straight for the boxes of toys in the far corner.

Dr. Abdul, a bubbly woman in her fifties, ushered us through to the equally empty Epilepsy and Non-Respiratory Sleep Disorder Clinic. She was dressed in layers of color, with a half-dozen small earrings up and down the length of her right ear. The purpose of the consultation, at Dr. Jensen's request, was to confirm the diagnosis of narcolepsy and obtain a second opinion on Mathilda's case. But by then, he had moved beyond any doubt that Mathilda had the condition, already prescribing her Modafinil as a first line of treatment for wakefulness and Gabapentin for her nightly ankle pain. For Oliver, this appointment was about Dr.

Abdul backing and supporting us. Any specialist worth his weight would confirm the urgency for effective treatment.

Dr. Abdul earned her reputation by the number of kids that had been referred to her over the years and that had been misdiagnosed with epilepsy. She was widely regarded as one of the few experienced doctors in the UK who specialized in treating children with insomnia, circadian rhythm disorders, restless leg syndrome and most significantly, narcolepsy. The children she treated were older than Mathilda, perhaps, but they displayed similar symptoms and similar needs. We both assumed that Mathilda's age and the severity of her symptoms would be the pivotal ga-mechangers. That a child so young and so crippled by the condition would qualify her for urgent intervention. But the clinician in me knew it might take some work, some convincing, if we were to come out of today's meeting with the golden ticket—a prescription for Xyrem.

Dr. Abdul, consultant clinical neurophysiologist, apologized for the length of hr waiting list and held open the door before offering Oliver and me both a seat. After watching the videos of Mathilda's cataplexy and countless episodes of her sleeping in random places like the kitchen floor, Dr. Abdul swung back round to us and began asking detailed questions. As we spoke, she took copious notes, recording major symptoms like ataxia, and minor issues such as incontinence and eating only at night, which had led to significant weight gain. She was also attentive to the strain on us as exhausted care-givers, and the challenges in managing Mathilda's meltdowns and uncontrollable anger. I was impressed with how thorough she was in covering every detail of the better part of the past year. I felt certain that such a detailed history would leave no doubt in her mind, that despite Xyrem being difficult to obtain, this child warranted every effort to obtain it. The MSLT, sleep-deprived EEG, and the sleep study were all deemed inconclusive. The only objective results she had to go on were the positive HLA-DBQ1 genetic marker test and the videos. Dr. Abdul went through the footage of Mathilda staggering and collapsing in the day and hallucinating at night a second time. We waited until she was satisfied with what she'd seen before she turned around, smiling.

"It's important that Mathilda refrain from high carbohydrate meals and pure sugars," she advised.

"That's going to be quite hard to implement because Mathilda has a very poor appetite during the day and craves all the wrong kind of foods throughout the night," I said, surprised that she wanted to start with secondary issues.

"We obviously try to give her a balanced diet," Oliver said, "but the reality is that her circadian rhythm is a mess, which interferes with her appetite control. She's very hungry through the night, and there's not a lot we can do about it," Oliver added whilst shifting in his seat. His anxiety was physical—shooting, localized back pain down his legs.

"Small, light snacks are the way to go. Also, at this age, breaking the day with planned twenty-minute naps would be helpful, although children often resist them since they don't want to appear different from their peers."

"Mathilda has no control over her daytime sleeping, when or where, let alone the length of naps," Oliver replied. I saw him raise his eyebrows, a look that betrayed a sense of disbelief. Dr. Abdul only heard the clipped tone of his voice.

"It is very important that she goes on to reach her educational potential and that the disorder does not interfere with her social development. From what you've said about her declining behavior, one of the most crucial things you can do is to keep on top of the discipline at home. Keep it consistent."

"Narcolepsy is affecting everything," I said, wanting her to acknowledge that we were working outside normal parenting parameters. "You can see how sleepy she is. She can't interact normally, or stay awake long enough to learn anything. She was starting to read before she became ill. That's all gone, and I obviously feel very pessimistic about her future." With the way things stood, I couldn't see how she would stay awake long enough to learn anything. In any case, those priorities had slipped beneath the pressing need to reach her in the dark place into which she had withdrawn and slowly pull her out. We knew Mathilda was in there somewhere. What we didn't know was whether or not we would find her again.

"On the plus side, episodes of cataplexy sometimes decrease spontaneously or once stimulant medication has started," Dr. Abdul offered, sounding positive.

"Really? When she's how old?" I queried.

"In older age, post-retirement, when less things are new and novel, and when there are fewer surprises in life."

"So less triggers? Toward the end of her life?" I asked skeptically, since I had not come across any indication that people with narcolepsy spontaneously recover. "Is that all she can look forward to? She's just turned four years old!"

"What are your thoughts on Xyrem, Sodium Oxybate?" Oliver asked, turning the conversation round, the way he always did when he felt it was a dead end.

"It's a good drug for some, but there's no need to rush into it. If Modafinil is not effective, I would try Ritalin or Dexamphetamine. Both stimulants are widely used in the treatment of narcolepsy. Xyrem isn't something I am that familiar with. It certainly isn't considered a first line of treatment for children like Mathilda."

"Modafinil works in that she has alert periods in the afternoons, but it does nothing for her ability to sustain restful sleep at night, and it makes her aggressive when she is awake. She was never an angry or wildly disobedient child. I think this is one of the hardest things. She is so unrecognizable now," I replied, trying to stay on top of my emotions.

"Our main concern is that she needs to be able to sleep at night," I continued. "I can't get away from that. From what we've learned, Xyrem can help people with their daytime symptoms as well. Stimulating her to stay awake in and of itself is not the solution. I'm worried she's becoming more tired as time passes, especially now that Modafinil keeps her awake in the afternoons. Xyrem is the only drug that will help her sleep at night, isn't it?"

There was a pause, an awkward break in the conversation, like I was stepping on the boundary between patient and doctor—something I was prepared to do. We needed her to believe in us and in what was happening inside Mathilda's brain. Dr. Abdul carried on as if she hadn't heard me.

"It's also important that every now and then she take a breather from treatment. Give her body a complete break from medication," she said, while simultaneously writing it all down. "I'll make these recommendations to Dr. Jensen, in addition to a baseline monitoring of her weight, blood pressure and growth, and an EEG every second year. Puberty comes early to children with narcolepsy. We will have to watch for that too."

"How early?" I was stunned, having never considered secondary sexual characteristics as a consequence of disrupted sleeping patterns.

"In narcolepsy, with the lack of NREM sleep and with the associated weight gain, she might start puberty by seven. There are drugs to offset this, but we can cross that bridge when we need to."

"Do you mean like full-blown puberty in the next few years? Periods, the whole lot?"

"It's likely, yes. I've read about it, and seen it in a few other children. But one thing at a time. I will get my recommendations sent over to Bristol and they can follow up with you from there, when you next see them," she said.

Dr. Abdul turned back to the screen, signifying the appointment was over. This new host of complex and challenging health issues, quite separate from narcolepsy, was utterly overwhelming. Although she was almost four years younger than Elliot, and six years younger than Liberty, soon there would be three children in our home, all going through puberty at the same time. How would I explain to Mathilda why her body was developing rapidly, catapulting her through puberty, when she was still occupied with playing with dolls?

"Where do we go from here?" I asked. "If you won't recommend Xyrem, who else can we see? She can't go on like this. Her quality of life is so poor and I'm not prepared to accept there's nothing better for her than this!" I lifted Mathilda in my arms and stood.

"Look at her!" I said, wiping the drool from Mathilda's mouth, the tears running down my face.

Dr. Abdul spun round and stood up, as if by standing in that tiny room in front of me would add weight to her final words.

"You need to focus on your parenting, Mrs. Crisp. That's the key here."

"I am focusing on it. But it's not realistic to expect that putting her on the naughty step will solve anything. She can't even walk straight some days!" I was a sentence away from swearing. The great hope of the meeting drained away with her every word.

"There are parenting courses you can both take to help figure out how best to manage her behavior. As I said, I'll send all these recommendations."

Defeated, irritated and frustrated, Oliver refused to make eye contact or small talk. He began picking up our bags, and lifting Mathilda's heavy legs onto the footrest of the stroller, he stepped toward the door. We were fully aware that our dealings with Dr. Abdul, a leading figure in childhood sleep disorders in the UK, had begun and ended there, in that room.

Back on the bus, leaving behind the historic buildings that mark out the city of dreaming spires, the two of us stared blankly ahead out of the window.

"I can't see how we are going to get through this without treatment. As if good parenting alone can make a differ- ence in any significant way. What a joke!" Oliver said under his breath, shaking his head slowly in disbelief.

"How can anyone call herself an expert in her field and deliver nothing other than a formatted monologue that doesn't address the problems Mathilda faces? She clearly has a very limited idea of what narcolepsy is." He bowed his head, covering his face with his hands, and began to cry silently, plaintive words trapped in his palms. "What's Mathilda's future?" he whispered. "Is this how they expect her to be for the rest of her life? How can we carry on not sleeping ourselves, caring for her twenty-four seven? How are we supposed to do that?" I shifted Mathilda deeper into my lap and reached across to Oliver's broad shoulders, stroking his neck.

"Knowing about a condition, even if you are an expert, is not the same as living with it," I answered, trying to prop him up although I was feeling exactly the same emotions he was—anger, mixed with disbelief and bitter disappoint- ment. "Today was a complete waste of time. I don't know who else to go to."

"There is no one else. She is the nation's expert. We are on our own. Getting Mathilda treated is on us." Oliver turned and took my hand, pressing it against his wet cheek. Then he lingered before raising my palm to his lips. "It's down to us," he said, turning my hand over. I felt the lasting warmth of his breath across my fingers before he lifted his head. And looking directly out of the bus window, crawling past the ancient colleges we both knew so well, he offered up a final realization.

"Claire, we are totally and utterly alone."

18 H1N1 VACCINE
Late October, 2010

> "It's our choices, Harry, that show what we
> truly are, far more than our abilities."
>
> —**J.K. Rowling**
> *Harry Potter and the Chamber of Secrets*

Ever since the children were old enough to sit in a high chair, Oliver had organized an early morning routine that he was religious about. He was a great believer in breakfast being the most important meal of the day, and on a deeper level, a bonding experience. It began around 7 a.m. with the table full of cereals followed by toast and fruit juice, and it ended with reading and prayers. To liven things up, he often switched on music we could sing along to before leaving the house, preparing us for the day ahead. There were a handful of times that year, particularly in the mornings, when I couldn't control my crying and didn't make it downstairs. One of the most unendurable aspects of caring for Mathilda was my own considerable lack of sleep. Until then, I hadn't known it was physically possible to survive on one or two broken hours of sleep a night. It turned out

I could. I could get dressed, I could brush the girls' hair, I could drive to the hospital. I could do almost all the practical tasks required of me—slower, perhaps, and with less accuracy, and almost always without color or joy. Nonetheless, things got done.

Neither by will nor by choice, I was aware of being swept into an emotional dimension where I began to entertain the attractive option of leaving. Such thoughts about walking away, just walking out of the house with nothing, not even a purse, plan or purpose, became singular moments of pleasure. With these fantasies, I procured minutes of mental relief in the visualization of escape. I discovered that a deep, albeit transient, pleasure could be found in being free from thinking, free from the nights of watching Mathilda hallucinate her three-year old way through the darkness. The idea of not being there was appealing. Perhaps if I walked far enough, I might see color again. I might feel sunshine burning the back of my neck. I might get wind of my family doing well, and of Mathilda having experienced some miraculous healing. And then I might turn around, and walk all the way back home. If the intransigent torment of sleep deprivation began to redefine the meaning of psychogenic pain, a sensation close to supreme anguish, those ideas of abandoning my family left a shameful aftertaste. I yearned for liberation, yet I was trapped with people who needed me, four people for whom I would give everything.

For the most part, the children's voices in the kitchen every morning were compelling enough for me to rearrange my face and be in the room, even if only as an observer. Like the proverbial fly on the wall, I could be present and watch the simple and beautiful moments of family life. I could hear the familiar sounds of tea being poured, and the prayer requests of Liberty and Elliot as they asked God to take Mathilda's 'floppies' away and for her to wake up long enough to play with them that day. Inevitably, when Mathilda registered her favorite cereal in front of her or a soundtrack she loved, she would succumb to cataplexy. Her head would drop down into her bowl, spilling its contents in her hair, unless one of us was quick enough to grab it out of her way. Other times, Liberty would stand behind her, holding her up under the shoulders whilst Oliver and I finished eating. We could have left her sleeping upstairs, yet somehow we all felt it was better to support her physically and have her with us rather than lose the essence of being a family. Somewhere along the line, we had made the decision to keep the kids laughing, even if it meant a cataplectic attack and all the physical dangers that came with it.

Knowing that her paralyzing trigger was happiness, perhaps we should have opted for a life without joy. But how could any of us seriously contemplate that? How could we tell the kids never to crack a joke, never to be humorous? How could we live without laughter and spontaneity? Then there were Mathilda's own efforts to control the varying degrees of paralysis. Sometimes she would clench her jaw, gritting her teeth down to stave off what might come next. Other times, when there was laughter, such as watching the older two dance to music, she would turn away and refuse to join in, knowing the sheer delight would render a full-blown collapse and acute embarrassment. What range of pleasures she managed to filter, I could not tell, but the transparency of her emotions was always a give-away. Sometimes the reverse happened. A gift she didn't like, such as a new dress, wouldn't have any effect on her muscle tone, and for that moment she was safe; her cataplexy didn't register. All this begged the question—in time, would she opt for mild contentment over joy? Would a low level of satisfaction be the closest thing to pleasure she would live with? Would depression set in as a dominant feature of her character and permanently misshape her disposition?

Even in my most disconnected moments, I witnessed a shift in all of our roles. Yet we all continued to lean on routines that framed each day. There were so many natural rhythms that were ingrained in our daily lives, such as quiet time after lunch and free play after the evening bath, that it took little effort on my part to keep Liberty and Elliot occupied. I had never given much thought to how important these rituals were. That year, I came to depend on them, grateful that such habits were part of a daily cadence that was now propping us all up. These hours at home became hooks that we hung our time on. They were recognizable hallmarks of our family as it used to be, and each of us was clinging to them in our own way.

Over the next few months, I continued attending outpatient appointments with the children in tow. Dr. Jensen asked how she was doing, and my answers were always the same. I pressed him about Xyrem, but his hands were tied with layers of red tape, bound by the limitations of socialized health care. My complex petition for treatment was floating somewhere between our conversations and the medical ethics committee that only met on occasion. At each visit, Dr. Jensen continued to remind me that a year's supply would cost our local health authority twelve thousand pounds. I acknowledged the considerable sum and risk, but I also put forth an argument explaining that his office understood Mathilda's symptoms only in part. Narcolepsy was a disorder that affected a small part of her brain, but every aspect of her life.

No one knew if Mathilda would tolerate Xyrem, or to what extent, if any, it would control the myriad of her symptoms. More than once, Dr. Jensen pointed out that she had been hit hard with the clinical tetrad specific to narcolepsy—hallucinations, cataplexy, sleep paralysis, and excessive daytime sleepiness. If having a full house of symptoms was some kind of badge of honor, as he put it, it wasn't enough to bolster our appeal for treatment, not now with Dr. Abdul's documented recommendation to improve our parenting skills and *wait it out*. He was right in noting that Xyrem had not been tested on children with narcolepsy as young as Mathilda, and that it was extremely expensive and difficult to secure. Yet none of these prohibitions were obstacles I thought couldn't be overcome. Although she might not tolerate the drug, or it might not be as effective as we hoped, she deserved to try it.

In our desperation, Oliver and I crafted a letter to our local Member of Parliament, Penny Hoffmeir, pleading Mathilda's case for comprehensive treatment. The letter specified her need for Xyrem and the detrimental impact her health was having on all of us. It was sent to the hospital management with Hoffmeir's demand for an explanation. Consulting with Dr. Jensen, the acting Chief Executive of Bristol Children's Hospital replied to the MP, acknowledging the investigations Mathilda had already undergone and stating that stimulant treatment, Modafinil, was already in place. Furthermore, he relayed that she had not experienced any delays in treatment or appointments, that a second opinion had been sought at Oxford, and that, given Mathilda's age, no one was inclined to initiate psychoactive medication. The outcome of that letter? She was now seen as an outpatient not every three weeks, but once every two weeks. Such was the NHS accommodation of our quest for effective treatment.

At our next appointment, the tension between us was evident, and you could cut the atmosphere with a knife. Dr. Jensen offered to call a colleague in Glasgow whom he had known from medical school, and who had experience with sleeping disorders in children. The conversation amounted to a phone call from the specialist's nurse with detailed information about low-fat food for children. Other than that, she said there was nothing else she could do since a face-to-face consultation had not been requested. With intense irritation, I barely managed to thank her for her time. Did she think diet alone would rectify or remedy her brain disorder? Would cutting carbs help Mathilda walk without falling, or quell her voracious appetite in the small hours of each night? Perhaps there was some validity in her advice, but it seemed to fall short of the magnitude of the situation. I wasn't in a place to re-design our menu plan and come up with seven new meals a week.

The day we spent in Oxford several weeks back drove Oliver forward. He looked for answers elsewhere, and he began to do that the only way he knew how. Through his line of work, and on the overseas job market, he started to explore securing the treatment and the expertise of a doctor who had both the experience and the confidence to treat a child as young as Mathilda. He knew that the odds of finding a theology job in the UK that fell within the local area of a pediatric sleep clinic were next to nothing. Operating on a postcode lottery system, access to specialists and treatment depended on where you lived—one of the many limitations of the National Health Service. Our other concerns had to do with the passage of time. It was possible that, over the next five to ten years, awareness of narcolepsy and access to treatment would emerge somewhere in England. In terms of Mathilda's childhood, it was gamble we felt would almost certainly be too little, too late.

One afternoon, he rang me from work, his voice unusually animated. I had spent the day preoccupied with the thought that Liberty and Elliot would be better off in school. They, too, had spent much of their time at the hospital, resulting in minimal direct supervision of their studies. As if on cue, I picked up the phone. He went straight to the point.

"Four teaching positions have come up in the US," he said.

"Four? Where are they?"

"Duke, Southern Methodist University, one in Illinois,

and another in California. They're all fairly close to what I do."

"Which one do you think looks like a good fit?" I said, hoping at least one of the options would line up with the field in which he worked.

"They're all pretty close. I could possibly apply for all four and go through the details with you tonight. What do you think?"

"Wouldn't you have to prove you are the only person who could do the job over and above an American applicant?"

"Yep."

"Oh." That seemed like impossible odds to me. "I don't know how we would go about getting treatment, though. How could we line up a job and the right doctor?"

"I don't know either, but it's a start. There's no harm in looking. We could perhaps run it by Mali and see if there is a sleep specialist near any of them. What do you think?"

"I think it's amazing. It's just hard to know what your chances are and how realistic any of this is."

I put the receiver down, and for the first time, began to feel a minuscule glimmer of optimism. That, and the few wakeful hours we had with Mathilda each afternoon, made tangible what at the time was a pipe dream. Aspiring to hope that there might be help somewhere, even as far away as the US, was enough to offset the dread of facing another night without sleep. For the first time in a long while, a future was possible wherein Mathilda might sustain more than a couple of daytime hours of wakefulness.

Less than a week afterward and late into a quiet evening, Mali called from Stanford. Foolishly, my thoughts jumped forward. Since it was foremost on our minds, I assumed she was ringing about Oliver getting a job in the US. Our evenings had been dominated with evaluating Oliver's various job options. I seized the opportunity to run the four locations by her, not considering she had called for a specific reason.

"That's so exciting. Keep me posted if anything works out," she said, after hearing me list the different opportunities for work and treatment in the US.

"Do you know of any pediatric sleep specialists in those states?"

"Not off the top of my head. But I would be happy to look into it. Actually, I was calling because we received Mathilda's blood yesterday, and the lab confirmed she has narcolepsy. This means she's the youngest diagnosed patient on record," she said, like this was good news.

"There are other young children with narcolepsy, though, right?" I asked. I did not process what she was telling me—that Mathilda's age might be a challenge, even for a US sleep specialist.

"Oh yes, we have a number of children, but none under

six. It is possible there are many more, just that they are not diagnosed."

"So why does she have it? I don't understand how or why she's been hit with narcolepsy when it doesn't usually occur in children her age."

"Well, that's really why I am calling. We have seen a significant increase in childhood cases of narcolepsy over the past six months. Not in the US, but all over Europe. There are clusters of children in Sweden and Finland, and possibly some in Ireland. The team here has been working on the possible reasons this might occur, and Professor Mignot wants me to run something by you."

"Sure," I said, confident I could give her anything she might ask.

"Claire, this might not be an easy question for you to answer. Did Mathilda receive the H1N1 vaccine?"

19 MOTHER'S GUILT
November 2010

"In this short life, that only lasts an hour, how much, how little is within our power."

—**Emily Dickinson**

I step out of our car parked within the grounds of Ashton Court. The children are already ahead, running hand-in-hand up the scraggy hill, past the deer that stand terrified. The older ones carry penknives to whittle any fallen branches into wands or miniature swords. The younger siblings trail, but not by much. Mathilda is there with them, lighthearted and loud, running carefree. There are toddlers, too, and babies in carriers. I hitch the picnic lunch across my back and begin jogging up the hill, leaving the cars to find Wendy, Mary, Sam and the others.

With my camera, I pause behind the twenty or so children and take a series of photos. There's Hannah, Bethany, and Liberty, each with a crown of golden leaves across their foreheads. I snap a line of boys balancing on a fallen tree above a leafy ditch, arms wrapped about the next shoulder, their voices echoing through the woods. They break up, taking turns challenging each other on the trunk with large sticks, like characters out of Robin Hood. Mathilda moves towards them, balancing behind Elliot. Her long blonde pigtails swing about her face, lit with a smile. She wears an old pair of red leather shoes, denim jeans with frills around the ankle and a striped hoodie. I take more photos of her standing there before she grabs Francesca's hand and chases after the older children, laughing.

She is three. She is healthy. She is a month away from the H1N1 vaccine. And in five years' time, that photo will be printed two million times and spread across newspapers in England. The headline —*Did the swine flu jab give little Mathilda a crippling sleep disorder?*

As our trips outside the house became fewer and farther between, Liberty and Elliot figured out a way to climb over our old stone wall and jump down into their friend Tash's garden. The wall itself was unstable in places, but just behind the shed several bricks were strong enough to make a ledge for a small foot, and the other side had been newly reinforced. Around this time, Liz, Tash's mum, stopped by and found me sitting in the lounge with Mathilda asleep on my lap. She would walk daily past our window on the way back from school, pushing her other daughter, Maddie, in the stroller. Every so often she would stop by to see how we were doing.

Today, having lost the concentration to read, I was playing an audiotape with the hope that Mathilda might hear some of it, though she was in and out of sleep.

Liz came in through the front door, knowing by now she could let herself in. I found myself explaining Gabapentin to her, the new drug that Mathilda was taking for her leg pain. Liz's husband was a local doctor, and I valued her quiet presence over cups of tea and the distraction of talking about other things.

That day, as Maddie was playing on the rug, Mathilda stirred from her nap and suddenly began screaming, grabbing the air in front of her.

"I can't see, Mummy, I can't see!"

"I'm right here. What do you mean?"

"I can't see anything, Mummy! Where are you?'

"I'm right here, Tilda, I'm right here." I turned her around to see me, holding her small face in my hands. "Look, see me now? I'm here."

"No Mummy, everything's black. I can't see anything. Where are you?" Liz saw tears well up in my eyes as I grabbed Mathilda by the shoulders, as if I could shake the blindness out of her. Maddie dropped the baby doll she was playing with and began to cry.

"Is she okay? Can I do anything to help?" Liz was up, terrified at the sudden outburst.

"I don't know what's wrong. This has never happened before. Her eyes are open but she can't see. She's never had this happen." I went on holding Mathilda and reassuring her, although I had no way of knowing when, or if, her sight would return. Too distraught to continue the conversation, I asked Liz to bring the phone. After scooping up Maddie, she left.

Within fifteen minutes or so, Mathilda's sight gradually returned, first her peripheral vision, then the colors and shapes of the room. The episode left my nerves frayed. I spent the next few hours holding her, waiting for Dr. Jensen to call back and praying that the blindness would not return when she next woke. When I spoke to him later and recalled what had happened, he was as baffled by the event as I was, suggesting the possibility that, like the rest of her body, her ocular muscles were exhausted, too fatigued to work. He seemed to offer explanations with the intention of settling my fears, yet much of what he said was devoid of any confidence or conviction. Dr. Jensen had prescribed Gabapentin several weeks back, a powerful medication used in the treatment of neurogenic pain. Its effect on Mathilda was negligible. Whatever new was going on in her body on top of the nightly hallucinations had rendered her anxious to the point where she began stroking parts of her body continually whenever she was awake. In desperation, I told this all to Dr. Jensen, stating how frightened I was that she was deteriorating, with further symptoms emerging. He suggested the physical touching of her body was a way of relieving stress. Though he attempted to allay my fears, he ended our conversation by explaining that he had been too busy to return any of Mali's emails.

If our appointment in Oxford was a watershed for Oliver, the blind episode was mine. With the possibility of a position in the US opening up, one that might secure treatment, we understood this much—it wasn't just that we *could* do it, but that, in the absence of specialist care for Mathilda, we *should* do it.

By now, Oliver was on his second round of Skype interviews at Fuller Theological Seminary just outside Los Angeles. On these occasions, he would sit at the kitchen table after a day at work and field questions from a panel of professors, some of whom appeared supportive of his application, and a few who didn't. It looked as though a physical visit would amount to us all flying to California in the New Year, though we weren't sure how we would get Mathilda there. One option was to travel to the East Coast, leave the children with our friends Luke and Gail Powery in New

Jersey, and then for Oliver and me to go on to California. We had misgivings about asking anyone to take care of her for several nights, but it was important we both visit Pasadena if he were offered the job. Leaving her in the UK with family was too risky. We would be gone for a week, and in the event of her needing us, the distance and time it would take to get back home felt irresponsible on our part.

Despite the hope that a new job would secure treatment for Mathilda, our wider concerns centered on Liberty's and Elliot's needs, and the enormous impact a move like this would have on their lives. I was acutely aware that their educational needs were not being met, not just in our present situation, but in the years to come. With the responsibility of three children's education weighing on me, I was forced to acknowledge that our days of home-schooling were coming to a close. On top of moving from a university in the UK to a Seminary 11,000 miles away and searching for a new place to live, Oliver, too, would accept that we also needed to find schools for all three children.

Within days, I learned that the blind episode was yet another symptom of narcolepsy—sleep paralysis. Because the ankle pain was still inexplicable, I was beginning to think the vaccine might have damaged her body beyond the symptoms of narcolepsy. Was it responsible for damaging more than her hypothalamus? Should we anticipate further symptoms to emerge over the next month or years? None of us knew what to expect next, and with the decision made to seek treatment in the US, it was time to find a doctor who would take her on. Mali had asked to speak to us again, and I took the opportunity to sound out her out.

"Oliver has an interview next month in Southern California," I said, one evening just before Christmas. "It would be very helpful to know if there was a pediatric specialist in the Los Angeles area. He has also applied for jobs in other states too, Illinois, North Carolina and Texas."

"There are people Professor Mignot works with all over the US, and we could look into that. But if you were to come to Southern California, he could be Mathilda's local doctor—and besides, the climate here is excellent for people with narcolepsy."

"But isn't it something like a seven-hour drive?" I asked, incredulous.

"It is, but with health insurance, that's close enough."

"Really?" I wanted to jump for joy. It had never occurred to me that Mathilda would have Professor Mignot as a "local" doctor. We knew so little of the way health care operated in America. We knew that we would have to pay for it, and we assumed that, in other ways, it ran on similar lines to the NHS—that accessing a specialist depended on where you lived. Changing the subject, Mali moved back to our previous conversation several days before.

"When did she have the vaccine, what month?"

"January. It was the 16th, just before I took her out of preschool."

"Professor Mignot is looking at a potential link between the sudden rise of narcolepsy in children throughout Europe and the H1N1 vaccine. Mathilda would be cited in some of the research papers he is going to publish, with your permission, of course."

"Yes, although I still don't understand how the vaccine caused her to develop narcolepsy." When I pressed Mali for more details, she clarified the position the researchers were currently maintaining. Along with other scientists, the team at Stanford was looking into what triggered the immune system to turn against itself and destroy the hypocretin cells in the hypothalamus—thus causing narcolepsy. Initially, it was thought that the adjuvant Squalene (a chemical added to the vaccine to enhance the body's immune response) had compromised the immune system. Much later, however, we discovered that it was more likely the vaccine itself was too strong. There were also other cases in the US where children had developed narcolepsy after direct exposure to swine flu, and not the vaccine.

"Professor Mignot believes the H1N1 virus itself may be involved in the mistake of the immune system," explained Mali. "The immune system went too far and mistakenly also killed the hypocretin cells. This has not been proved with certainty, though," she said in conclusion. "I'm sorry we can't give you a more concrete answer at this point." I knew narcolepsy was an autoimmune illness and that, in addition to the trigger, Mathilda carried the genetic marker for narcolepsy, along with 25% of the general population. I also knew she hadn't been directly exposed to swine flu itself. None of us had.

In the years since that phone call with Mali, I have deliberated, rationalized and wept over the boundaries between accountability, responsibility and guilt. Time and again, Oliver has consoled me, reminding me that it was *our* decision—that we leaned on the sure advice from the government and did what any responsible parent would have done with that information. In Europe, none of the parents who chose to immunize their children with the 2010 H1N1 vaccine knew that the vaccine was too strong. More importantly, they did not know that it had not been tested on children. They did not know that it would cause the body to turn against itself, destroying cells within the hypothalamus and resulting in a lifelong neurological condition. What I continue to weigh within my heart is that *I* booked the appointment. *I* took her there. *I* pressed Mathilda's arm in my hand as I pinned her still in a clinic full of trusting children on their mother's laps. I hear myself thanking the doctor for making the experience smooth and painless, for giving Mathilda a vaccination that would keep her out of hospital should she ever be exposed to swine flu.

With an insufferable burden of self-reproach I feel the desperate need to control time, to reach back and erase it all. If only that was a maternal gift I could bestow upon her. When I finally grasp that such a notion is absurd, I start that day again in my mind and replay the morning. Only this time, I take a detour and do not drive to Fishponds Family Practice. Instead, we go to the park only two blocks away from the clinic. I think Mathilda should wear her coat because the distant sound of thunder means that rain is on its way. But she is too distracted by the excitement of other children running wildly through the play structures. Then, climbing up on to the swing, Mathilda pumps her legs back and forth, squealing with the delight of a typical three-year old. I stand in front of her, ready to push both knees away again as she begs "Higher, higher!"

One of the other parents passes the time of day with me for a few minutes and I engage with her because although Mathilda is happy, she doesn't need to be held or watched. As the swing slows she is holding fast to the chains and leans back, closes her eyes, then lifts her face to the rain.

20 HOPE
January 2011

"No act of kindness, however small, is ever wasted."

—Aesop
The Lion and the Mouse

It was late January. The five of us boarded a British Airways flight to Newark, and then traveled on to Princeton by train, retracing our journey two and a half years earlier when we had moved to Ross Stevenson Circle just a few doors down from Luke and Gail Powery. Only this time, we arrived not in the thick afternoon humidity but late into the night, cognizant of an earlier winter storm and ten feet of snow banked up on the sidewalks—more was forecast. Back in the summer of 2008, both families' children were inseparable. Libby with their daughter Moriah, and Mathilda with "Big Zackwy," both two years old—attending preschool together, playing outdoors on bikes and stealing themselves away to draw on the walls of our rented house, giggling as they did so. Gail and I had been there, pretending to be cross, wishing they could stay like that forever, that having a time-out on the naughty step might be the worst thing that ever happened to them.

Now, returning with Mathilda visibly altered, we explained what care she would need over the next five days and four nights. I had forgotten how many stairs they had directly behind the front door. One flight up to the living area and another down into the basement, where the bedrooms were. Mathilda seemed to remember aspects of their home and their faces but made almost no attempt to engage with anyone, not even Zachary. Luke and Gail had already decided to share the nights between them, setting up a bed for Mathilda in the playroom upstairs so they could nurse her from the guest room opposite. They had also cleared their schedules and found extra snow gear for the children knowing for the next week, they would be virtually housebound. The following morning, Oliver and I took a flight across the country to Los Angeles—the City of Angels. Our thoughts turned to the days ahead in the knowledge that Mathilda would be well cared for in Princeton and that the outcome of the interviews would determine her health and all of our futures. The six-hour flight gave us time to discuss what questions might come up and how much we wanted to inform the hiring committee about our situation. Landing at LAX, we were struck by the warm and balmy weather, typical of Southern California that time of year. I had heard about the congestion and overpopulation in LA but it didn't seem to be so different from Bristol, just that here everything was dry and tinted with sunshine, the grass on the banks of the freeway, the color of straw. What surprised me was the vastness of the mountains to the north, the brilliance of the light that played upon them and the verdant yards of Pasadena, streets lined with palm trees and the faint odor of citrus.

If our nightly nursing of Mathilda over the last year had any payoff, it was that our bodies didn't register that we were in a different time zone. Neither one of us felt the added effects of jet lag, either across to the East Coast or now on the West. But we had learnt to recognize extreme levels of exhaustion in ourselves and in each other—when we were close to being dysfunctional. For me it meant I would cry without good reason—and have almost no control in stopping. The slightest thing might set me off, like the distant sound of an ambulance siren when the very thought of someone being hurt or injured wrought havoc with my emotions. Other times I would notice a loss of short-term memory and have no recall of what had just happened or what someone had just said—meaning that I would also repeat myself over and over, much to everyone's frustration. Then, on particularly bad days, when my attention and focus was so poor, I had minor accidents—cutting myself chopping up vegetables, backing the car into a lamp post and then into our low front brick wall.

Oliver had become adept at identifying these signs of sleep deprivation and would insist on covering Mathilda's care that night and for as long as needed, by which time I would then do the same for him—take the night shift alone. Emotionally, he seemed to be holding us all together, but cognitively he felt his head was wrapped in cotton wool, as though he was walking around in a permanent fog. His writing slowed up to the point where he became months behind on deadlines and contracts with publishers. He forgot important meetings, and neglected emails—unable to keep up with many professional demands that extended beyond the classroom. But the more immediate and pressing signs of sleep deprivation manifested itself by mimicking the symptoms of flu. He would suffer body aches, chills and almost all the signs of coming down with something, but without the fever. It was a signal that he wouldn't make it through to the evening without a long nap. If he was at work, he would crash in his office between meetings and classes. Failing that, after cycling home I could see he needed to go straight to bed, often waking around 8 p.m. feeling wretched.

On our journey westward, neither of us had managed to shake off the detrimental side effects of sleep deprivation and it was on such a morning that Oliver woke up to begin a three day intensive run of campus interviews. Dosing up on painkillers and anti-inflammatories helped take the edge of his symptoms to the point where he was able to field questions and complete the interview process we hoped without anyone noticing. The appointing committee also wanted to watch him in the classroom, assess how he communicated and interacted with students so they had scheduled for him to teach as well as sit a theology examination. At the same time, the Dean, a distinguished, silver-haired man named Howard Loewen had set me up with Chris, a realtor (estate agent) who, on our second day, gave me a tour of Pasadena and surrounding areas, even taking me inside several homes so I could get an idea of the kind of place we might live in, should it all work out. With Chris doing all the driving, I relaxed enough to process whether Pasadena might be workable. Knowing that we had three children, she showed me parks and pools along the way, places that might be of interest like libraries and movie theaters. In South Pasadena, driving away from the main road not dissimilar from a high street in a British town, she pointed out the local hospital although it was the last place I wanted to see. The valet service made it look more like a hotel than a hospital but I wanted to believe that Mathilda's days of being hospitalized were over—that being here and receiving treatment from Stanford would mean we might all live something that resembled "near-normal life."

It so happened that my maternal uncle Fred lived on Redondo Beach just outside of LA and had scheduled a mini coastal road trip on our last day, starting at Santa Monica and ending down at Palos Verdes—by his favorite golf course. I sat in the back of the car between his ex-wife Darlene and ex-girlfriend Mari—the tension between them diffused partly by the stunning coastline and partly by Fred's magnetic personality. Few people could pull off such a complex array of relationships but if anyone could, Fred was your man. Ironically, the last time we had seen him was the first day Mathilda was hit with Excessive Daytime Sleeping (EDS), when she couldn't wake up at his party in London eighteen months previously. Now sitting at a beach cafe, watching stereotypical Californian beach bodies play volleyball, we were able to ask him what it was really like to live here.

"In La-La land?" He said in his broad cockney accent. "I love it and hate it. I love the weather, the people, the year-round golf, the lifestyle. But I hate how expensive it is, and how little time off you get. I work all year for a two-week break—it's not enough, so I am thinking of working for myself, setting up a kitchen design company so I can get back to the UK when I want to. If you move here, you need to be prepared for that—to work your arse off," he said.

That last day, several hours before our flight back to New Jersey, Oliver and I were expected to meet with Howard in his office on campus. We imagined he would ask us about the practical side of relocating, getting the five us and some of our things over to California and the possible timeline. But it was also intensely important to me to be up front about our reasons for being there. From a career perspective, it wasn't an obvious move for Oliver and he had already come up against widespread criticism from colleagues back home who thought he would stay at Bristol for a few more years before being headhunted by Oxbridge. A switch now to a Seminary was career suicide in their eyes. As word got round that he was away interviewing at an institution quite different from a British university, there was a well-meaning, universal sense that he had gone mad. One senior colleague, Elizabeth Archibald, a Professor of English was more understanding, acknowledging what a move like this might cost him.

"This is the right thing for your family," she said one morning standing outside their offices at Bristol University. "Things will open up for you later, but you are right to consider going now, when your daughter's needs take precedence." It wasn't that Oliver was in two minds or in any way conflicted because the overwhelming priority as we saw it was to get Mathilda treated, but still, it was a hard decision to make and the reaction from colleagues was on very tired days, difficult to bear. Given his private nature, he never let on how sick Mathilda was, just that she had been in an out of hospital, and that treatment for her condition was not available to us in Bristol. Details of her condition and the impact it was having on us he concealed from almost everyone. The hiring committee at Fuller might question his motives too and during our meeting with Howard Loewen I raised the issue of Mathilda's narcolepsy, not only because I wanted to be transparent but also to understand how Fuller's health care scheme worked. It was one thing to land the job, quite another to line up all the other components that would secure her treatment under Professor Mignot. I was worried that our situation was so complicated, and that there were too many parts to it, that Howard couldn't guarantee would work even if they wanted to appoint Oliver. If the medical world had never seen a three-year old child with narcolepsy before, how would the health insurance company deal with it? Would they permit us to access Stanford? And would our insurance cover the cost of Xyrem, priced in the US at over $3,000 a bottle? Howard wasn't sure how or if it would all come together, there were so many variables, but something he said at the end of our conversation gave me confidence that Fuller could handle a complex transatlantic hire.

Another academic Englishman, John Goldingay, had brought his wife Anne to Pasadena from Nottingham twenty years previously. She was suffering from Multiple Sclerosis and had needed a similarly complex medical care arriving wheelchair-bound and tube-fed. Although we wouldn't meet John for another six months, Howard had relayed how Anne received excellent health care right up until she passed away several years after arriving in California. The fact that they had successfully transferred from the UK with Fuller's help made me think if it could be done once, maybe it could be done again. Howard's last words to us as we left his office that morning would stay with me over the next months, when Oliver and I would make the final decision to emigrate.

"If getting Mathilda the right care is important to you both, then it's important to us. We'll make it work," he said.

I do not know how confident Howard really was, issuing a promise like that to a family like ours, but I do know now that it was enough for us to think that moving to America was a risk worth taking. That night, waiting in the departure lounge at LAX with Oliver, a profound sense of peace came over me. Filtering out the constant announcements, and the shuffling of several hundred bodies close to mine under gate 25, I understood that here might be a place where I would see Mathilda again. The old Mathilda. The child who chattered her way through meal times, put her tiny hands round my neck and who ran along walls. The little lady as we called her who might again do something as simple as sleep at night. Staring down at the boarding pass in my hand, I didn't want to return to London Heathrow, or anywhere in England, to the grueling cycle of exhaustion and the pointless hospital appointments, doctors who for the past year had written us both off. I wasn't sure I could do it, not even for a few more months. And then, looking up through the glass walls reflecting the city lights, I experienced a moment believing that something incredible might happen. That as well as sleeping at night, Mathilda might wake up during the day. And in her waking, the shame I had felt over the last year at craving sleep for myself above everything else made sense. I was trying to survive. I was trying to make sure we all stayed together. Of course this flame of hope was contingent upon a long chain of events lining up, like dominoes, where every piece had to stand its own ground. The slightest hiccup with the job process, health insurance, Stanford, and Mathilda's response to treatment and this move would all be for nothing. I tried to hold on to that feeling as I sat down and lifted the shutter of the small oval window. Soon the blaze of Los Angeles faded beneath the aircraft and feeling safer thirty thousand feet above sea level than I had done anywhere else in the last year, I reached for Oliver's hand, and without speculating on Fullers' decision, the two of us fell into a deep sleep.

21 THE CITY OF ANGELS
July 2011

> "Go back? he thought. No good at all. Go sideways,
> impossible! Go forward? Only thing to do!" So up
> he got, and trotted along with his little sword held
> in front of him and one hand feeling the wall, and
> his heart all of a pitter patter.
>
> —**J.R.R. Tolkien**
> ***The Hobbit***

As it turned out, we didn't hear from Howard or anyone on the hiring committee for eight weeks. We told ourselves that a delay in being offered the job reflected our ignorance of US employment procedures and not a failure on Oliver's part to secure the position. But both of us had expected to hear sooner, and, with our lives in limbo, those winter weeks were the darkest I can remember. We had learnt from our two previous stints in the US that the visa process was uncertain and was not amenable to last minute applications. Also, all five of us would have to interview at the American Embassy in Grosvenor Square, London, before any concrete plans could be made. And Fuller would have to prove that Oliver was the sole candidate who could do the job, over and above any American. If this could be done and he was offered the post as Professor of Systematic Theology starting in August, it would mean a tight turnaround, not only for tying up our lives in England, but also for processing the legal documents we needed to stay in the US longer than three months. Added to that, we had to figure out Mathilda's health insurance and work with Mali. She had warned me that Professor Mignot had a small patient list, and the few clinical hours he offered on Wednesdays were booked up well in advance. Alongside a team of scientists, his main focus was on researching the cause of narcolepsy and finding better treatments—perhaps even preventing the condition from developing in predisposed people. At no point did Mali ever talk about a cure.

With the two of us on tenterhooks, Oliver repeatedly checked his email, and I stalled telling our families about a decision that would impact their lives profoundly. I knew that they would understand our reasons for leaving. I knew that they had watched from a distance, pained at the unraveling of Mathilda's health. I knew that they felt for all of us. Without a concrete decision to move, we carried on with the immediate demands of each day and night; we trusted that, one day, there would be a break in Mathilda's unrelenting torment.

The call finally came just before Easter, and the relief we both felt was palpable yet tinged with the logistical burden ahead. Maybe Mathilda would receive the help she needed there. It might take several years to see an improvement in her health and to settle into a new life in the US as resident aliens. For now, there was the long line of hoops to jump through and the administrative hurdles to overcome, all weighed against the uncertainty of how she would respond to treatment. Still, this single strand of hope we had gave us the strength to coordinate the details of emigrating, working through what became a full time job over the next few months.

By now it was May, and I went into organizational mode, finding the capacity to plan, pack up and make the necessary arrangements in selling our house. The financial overheads were a complete unknown since there were so many complex layers between the cost of insurance, hospital visits and medications, let alone the massive expenditure of relocation. And unbeknownst to us then, there would be three surgeries within that first year. Mali had talked us through the different health insurance options. I understood vaguely that we would have to choose between the Health Maintenance Organization (HMO) and the Preferred Provider Organization (PPO). The HMO granted us access to specific hospitals and doctors, while the PPO, although considerably more expensive, offered flexibility when it came to choosing a specialist. She also mentioned Medicaid, the recent changes in Obamacare and the Sheldon Drug Store (SDS) pharmacy in Missouri—the only dispensers in of Xyrem in the US. But all of it was as clear to me as a foreign language. There was no way of wrapping our heads around the shifting American medical system within the time we had left in the UK, and I gave up trying. I knew only that some people paid thousands of dollars each month for Xyrem, that others couldn't get their hands on it at all, and that still others battled with changing policies thrown at them by their insurance companies. I had a list of questions around our own need for Xyrem. How would it get to us? What fraction of it, if any, would be covered by our insurance policy?   But the biggest questions at stake were whether or not Mathilda would even respond to the medication, and if it would allow her restful sleep at night and reduce her excessive daytime drowsiness. On an intrinsic level as a mother, I understood only that going to the US, selling everything we had and risking our futures was necessary—that I couldn't live with myself unless I tried. We wanted our daughter and our lives back. It was that simple. Weighed against the risks, Oliver and I would have to trust that all the details would work out in our favor.

Another more immediate concern was persuading Liberty, then twelve, that the move was right for all of us. She didn't want to leave everyone and everything she knew and loved. She was happy.

"I don't want to go," she said after I broke the news to her and Elliot one quiet evening.

"Unless we can come back," she added.

"We can't promise that. But I do think it's the right thing for all of us. And if it were you or Elliot that needed treatment, we would do the same thing. I'm sure there'll be many new friends and opportunities for you there," I said, hoping she would understand in part at least.

"It's a beautiful place, and we can keep home schooling for as long as possible," Oliver said, holding her. "Are there things we can do to help you?" he asked.

"No. There's nothing. Only a dog would help."

The promise was out before he'd even thought it through.

"Okay. We can get you a dog. What kind would you like?"

And with that, Elliot, always the peacemaker and with an entirely different take on things, stood and said, "Mathilda needs treatment, Libby. It's not Princeton, but it is America."

To our relief, Fuller had an apartment we could rent for as long as it took us to find a place of our own. Our fares would be covered, and there was a provision to ship over the essentials. For our family, that meant books, kitchen stuff and the children's toys, as well as a leather armchair, a large rug that once belonged to my parents and the piano they had given us. In moving around over the years, we had learnt to travel light and pack according to the destination's climate. And that's what we did. Leaving our wet weather gear, winter coats, boots and heavy bedding, we gathered only a small wardrobe of summer clothes, which kept within the baggage allowance for a transatlantic flight.

It was with a modicum of satisfaction that I took Mathilda to what would be her last appointment with Dr. Jensen. I repeated the journey through the city, parked a half-mile away and pushed her through the underpass and into the elevator of Children's Hospital. It was late in the afternoon, always a quiet time in the pediatric outpatients' clinic. The smells of antiseptic mixed with unpleasant odors were the same as ever, but I realized that this time might be the very last time we would make that trip. The different families in the waiting area still intrigued me. I recognized some of the children in their customized wheelchairs, some with an obvious defect like hearing loss or a neurological disorder. Like Mathilda, I suspected a few had largely invisible conditions.

After a short wait, Dr. Jensen appeared suddenly beside us.

"You'd never miss an appointment would you? Not even be late for one," he remarked, seeming slightly irritated. Baffled by his comment, I followed him into the same side room we had always met in and sat down. Perhaps my inherent belief in the National Health Service and his role as Mathilda's advocate meant I was holding on to the outside chance that the application for Xyrem had come through at the eleventh hour. It was hard to give up this innate conviction that the Health Service that had given Mathilda the vaccine would be the same Health Service that would help assuage some of the symptoms. This was the NHS, my former employer, and one of the foundational institutions on which post-war Britain was built. What was I expecting? That Dr. Jensen would tell me now that we wouldn't have to up-sticks and drastically alter the course of our lives? That the past year had been an unfortunate miscommunication on all fronts—a colossal misreading of Mathilda's situation? That they were sorry for giving up on her a few months back and referring us to the psych unit? That they would provide the treatment she needed? Already our house was on the market, an attorney in LA was working on our visas and Mali was willing to hold an appointment open for Mathilda in July. Oliver was a week away from handing in his notice. I realized that Dr. Jensen had nothing new to say, and I went straight to the point.

"Oliver has been offered a job in California that we anticipate will secure treatment for Mathilda. We're going to take it."

"What about his career?" he said, looking up at me. He was stunned that Oliver would leave the University of

Bristol, especially for a job that was a demotion in his eyes. His comment betrayed his lack of understanding of our immediate situation and of a future without Mathilda's symptoms under control.

"We both know it's the right thing to do," I answered, not wishing to be drawn into details.

"Bit of a risk, isn't it, taking your family over there? No one's ever treated a four-year-old narcoleptic, you know that? Not even Stanford."

"It is a risk," I answered quickly. "But so is staying." And with that, I shed any residual notion that he, or any other doctor there, would deliver treatment in time to restore Mathilda's childhood. I recall little else from that appointment other than finally resisting the urge to tell him what I really thought—that his team and the system they worked within had ultimately failed her. Instead I paused, stood up and reached over the desk to shake his hand. And without looking back, I pushed Mathilda out through the waiting area. Stroking her long hair off her face, I told her that neither of us would ever have to go back there.

Right up until that last week when the packers came and after our families bid us farewell, we tracked our visa status online, desperately hoping they would arrive on time. Our flight with Air New Zealand was booked already, leaving forty-eight hours between our arrival in Los Angeles and our appointment with Professor Mignot up in Palo Alto. But without the legal documents in our hands, we would find ourselves grounded in the UK, having to forfeit both flights and the appointment at Stanford. According to the London-based American Embassy, the H2 visas would arrive in time for the flight. The precise delivery date was down to the Royal Mail, which, as it happened, delivered the precious paperwork the evening before we left.

Over those last few days, I shifted between cleaning the house and selling our new Mazda to giving away our beds and further farewells to our friends and neighbors. Throughout those final hours, I felt as though the imaginary rope I had been clinging onto all this time was slowly being raised towards the top of the cliff. I held on to the tangible hope of treatment ahead of us, even if it meant facing a million unknowns. There were moments when the rope plunged a few feet, and with that came a primitive fear that threatened my grip. My hand would slip an inch every time I asked *why. Why narcolepsy? Why her when she's so young? Why not me when I have already had my best years and am willing to endure the symptoms?* I threw this question at God and at Oliver, who answered me gently, "Why *not* us?" His response curbed my anger, but it did nothing for my anguish. Then, with every small piece of good news, like being lent a car once we arrived in CA, I felt the rope hitch, with Mathilda and I still clinging to it. At some point, I sensed we would reach the top of the rock cliff and crawl to a place of safety. Medication would assuage her symptoms enough for me to drag her up and over the edge into hours of wakefulness, and she would have her life back. Then the closing run of events, packing and walking through our family home and garden, saying goodbye to it all, and the painful last conversation with my parents, left me plummeting down again. And thus it continued.

Getting from Bristol to Heathrow airport required herculean efforts, and not just on our part. Though experienced in driving through bad weather, the coach driver was struggling to navigate the packed bus of travelers on the M4 safely in a torrential rainstorm. The water hitting the windows and the condensation inside the bus obscured the view of the surrounding countryside. The traffic slowed, and we missed our check-in time. What we didn't anticipate was a 24-hour delay on our flight. The designated aircraft had been struck by lightning on landing and needed a team of engineers to check that it was safe to make the flight back across the Atlantic. Fearing we would not make the appointment at Stanford, Oliver and I pleaded with the Air New Zealand personnel to be transferred to another flight, one that would depart that same day. Their only offer was that two of us could fly ahead of time. We discussed the option of one adult and Mathilda going ahead, but given the magnitude of the move on all of us, we thought it best to travel together.

Our best man Peter and his wife Christina, along with their children Lauren and Annabelle, had already planned to meet us for lunch in one of the airport restaurants. After hearing our dilemma, they offered to drive us all back to their house in London for the rest of the afternoon; we would return to a hotel later that night. Since our bags were checked in, and upon realizing I hadn't put Mathilda in training underwear, we accepted the offer of extra time with them and the use of their washing machine. Somehow, by early evening, they managed to put a roast dinner for nine on the table, a token last supper that surpassed anything we had eaten in months. We tried our best to relax and enjoy a few extra hours of their company and the temporary distraction from the journey ahead.

Returning to the airport the next morning, we boarded what would be an uneventful flight from London to LAX, not knowing when the five of us would see England again. Oliver repeatedly checked we still had our passports and visas on hand as though in the last few minutes he may have mislaid them. And I insisted that Libby and Elliot hold tightly to the carts whilst carrying their own little backpacks. Having deprived the children of a TV for the past ten years, the in-flight entertainment along with the bags of coloring books we'd packed meant the hours sped by. Liberty had withdrawn into her window seat, surrounding herself with a stony silence as Oliver and I took turns taking Elliot to the bathroom. He had developed stomach flu just hours before, demanding tag team parenting on our part to avoid him throwing up over any of us. Early on in the flight, I reached over to Mathilda and helped her with the headset and controls.

"Is it okay if I watch this Mamma?" she asked.

"Of course. Flying is so fun. You get to watch as much as you like. Remember last time when you went to Zachary's house and we took you on the plane?"

"No. When did we go?"

"About six months ago. Remember all the snow? Well, it's going to be beautiful and sunny in California, so that'll be different, but I think you'll like it. Plus, you'll have new medicine to help you feel better," I said, trying to reassure her and convince myself as though it was a self-fulfilling prophecy.

"But I don't like medicine, and I won't be able to swallow pills," she said.

"The new medicine is a liquid, so all you have to do is drink it. You'll be able to do that right?"

Then she was gone again. Asleep and drooling, her head rested on my lap while the sound of cartoon characters chirped through the headphones.

Eleven hours later, after meeting with the US immigration officers and explaining our bizarre situation, including why we were there without a return ticket, we collected our bags from the conveyer belt. Piling them high on several carts, we made our way through the unusually empty terminal that Sunday morning, July 17, 2011, one day before Mathilda's fifth birthday. Eighteen months had passed since the onset of symptoms. Finally, we were within reach of assuaging her suffering. From inside the terminal, Elliot pushed her toward the exit. Oliver took the largest cart. Packing away our newly stamped passports and paperwork, he asked if I was ready. I paused to take Liberty's hand, and then I nodded. Stepping out through the automatic doors and into the brilliant light, the five of us squinted, arrested by the sun's blaze and intense heat rising off the tarmac. As cabs pulled up and cars pulled away toward the freeway, we were surrounded with the emotional reunions of fellow travelers.

I once thought I understood how life worked, its purpose and my place in the grand order of things. That a fierce determination to work hard and make sense of my purpose meant I would never be somewhere more terrifying than I could cope with. Anything demanded of me would be do-able, and whatever the task, I would do it well. I didn't know then where the edge was or how closely we would come to it. Neither did I have any perception of our physical and spiritual limitations—how much longer I could hang on without sleep or a sense of perspective. What I had anticipated was a journey, not without suffering or immunity from adversity, but one that would be more familiar, a road somewhat well-trodden. Illusions of controlling the trajectory of the children entrusted to my care were merely that—illusions. I had no jurisdiction over any of it, I never had. Standing at the exit of LAX with our suitcases loaded onto two carts, I crouched down to unbuckle and wake Mathilda.

"Is this America? Can I get out?" she asked.

"Yes, we're here," I answered, lifting her from the seat of the stroller. She took a few steps before wobbling, her knees giving out on the busy crosswalk. Sensing a fall, I dodged the heavy traffic and scooped her up, feeling her weight to be that of a child many years older. Trailing behind the others on the crosswalk with her head bobbing against my shoulder, I experienced a moment of profound peace and offered a prayer of gratitude. It was the same quietness that had come to me intermittently since the very first hospital admission—a stillness that didn't reorder the past, could never change it, but that would be enough for us all going forward.

"It is good," she whispered. And with that, we continued our steps into the dazzling light of Los Angeles toward the mountains that would become our home.

22 DREAM
Summer 2014

"Little puppet made of pine, awake.
The gift of life is thine."

—Carlo Collodi
Pinocchio

I found Dr. Shah four years later. By then we were on opposite sides of the world. It was intensely important to me to thank him for sweeping into our lives for those few brilliant hours in May of 2010. I wanted to let him know how Mathilda was doing, that she was on treatment but that we had to leave our home in order to secure it. His response reached me via email in California early one hot, August morning as I sat drinking coffee in our front yard.

Dear Claire, Mathilda and family,

I am delighted for all of you. I do remember seeing you on the renal ward at the Children's Hospital and then us meeting up at CIU. I am extremely happy that Mathilda received the appropriate treatment and has grown into a smart young lady!

I am humbled by your kind words. I cannot describe how much it means for you to take the effort to find my email and write to me.

I have left Bristol and relocated in India (my hometown Ahmedabad). The fewer resources and less training opportunities out here means I have a greater chance to diagnose and manage sick kids with neurological disorders who need it.

Please keep me updated on the progress.

Best Wishes,

Siddarth.

In my email I had also attached a photograph of Mathilda that was taken a few weeks before. She and I had driven several miles from our house to the Huntington Gardens in Pasadena, just outside Los Angeles. Walking past waterfalls and through the rose garden, we found ourselves seated on a shaded terrace. Above us, an arbor dripping with purple wisteria framed the idyllic Japanese garden and perfectly arched bridge just a few feet away. I told Mathilda about the dream, a recurring vision I had back in Bristol when she was at her worst.

"You tried so hard to reach the top of the bridge but your legs kept giving way and you felt too sleepy to make it over the other side," I said, taking her hand.

"Really? You had a dream about me?" Mathilda asked.

"I did. I had the same dream over and over. Your friends were on the other side of the bridge cheering you on. You wanted to play with them, but at first it was really hard for you to climb to the top."

"Did they have narcolepsy?" she asked.

"No, but they understood you did, and they didn't care because they really wanted to be with you. And they waited and cheered so you would get all the way over and meet them on the other side."

"Wow, Mum! That's an awesome dream," she said.

"I know. It seemed so real, like it was really happening. Then I saw you let go of the rail and find the strength to run down the other side. Really fast. Mathilda, you ran as fast and as strong as you could. Some of you friends stood and clapped and called your name. You didn't feel floppy, you didn't have cataplexy. You just ran and started laughing as you heard them all calling for you to join them."

I told her how the grass was jeweled, sparkling like emeralds in the sunshine, and how she gradually became more and more awake, enough to recognize faces in the crowd. Circling the bridge in the water below were Koi fish popping up and down, their mouths wide open. We talked about how hungry they were and the kinds of things they might eat all day. Mathilda pointed to the exotic flowers on the low bank and in a matter-of-fact fashion said that they were the same as the tall flowers that grew in our little garden back home.

"No sweetheart. These plants need a lot of sunshine and not too much water. It's different here. So that means different things thrive." She leaned heavily into me, turning the ring on my wedding finger round several times before looking up.

"What does thrive mean?" she asked.

"It means growing well, and being the best you can be given the limitations you are working with," I answered, knowing some of what I said might be lost on her.

"Was it this bridge that I walked on?" she asked, swinging her legs under the bench.

"I'm sure it was."

"Did you know it was here? Before we came to California?"

"No. I'd only ever seen it in my dream. But the bridge seemed real, and seeing you run over to the other side gave me hope," I replied.

"Didn't you know I would get better?" Mathilda asked, looking up at me.

"Daddy and I were not sure if you would respond to treatment, but we hoped so. And hope is very powerful."

"How is it powerful, Mumma?"

"It's like an arrow that shoots into the future sending a message of promise, of good things that will happen," I answered. "So we hoped you would do better and flourish and grow, like these flowers, even though we know there isn't a cure for your narcolepsy. And we thought the best way to help you was to come and get the treatment you needed."

"They should let kids on there," Mathilda said, fascinated by the wooden gate at the foot of the bridge that forbade anyone from entering.

"Why is it locked? I'd *really* like to walk over it. They should let all the kids in," she said.

"What do you think would happen if they let people trample on the bridge?" I asked her.

"It would get ruined."

"Yes. You are right. It would get damaged, and then looking at it would be spoilt because it would no longer be perfect. Like when we pick flowers that die and then no one can see how beautiful they are," I said, smiling and holding her.

"But it would be really fun. I could show you how fast I can run." Standing up, Mathilda jogged on the spot, pumping her arms as if to prove herself, her tongue momentarily bulging out the rim of her bottom lip.

"I'm sure you could. But you don't need to sweet girl," I said, pulling her down on to my lap and kissing her temple lightly.

"Besides, you already have."

"I'd still like to try," Mathilda replied, refusing to give up on her idea. We lingered there a while. The gardens in front of us and the mountains to our left framed the only home she would ever remember.

"I know you would," I said in response. "But, my darling, once is enough."

EPILOGUE

Two days after landing in LA, we drove Mathilda from our new apartment in Pasadena to Palo Alto. It was a scorching, hot day, her 5th birthday, as it happens. Yet, we were more preoccupied with the challenges of driving in heavy traffic and foreign roads through the Angeles National Forest. We'd borrowed a car from our friends, Nicole and Darian Lockett, who took Liberty and Elliot back home with them to Orange County until our return from the bay area. Not only that, but Nicole had left a care package in the front passenger seat—a bag that included coloring books, snacks, and above all, water. Weaving along the freeway through the vast, barren hills with the sun beating down on their old Honda Civic, Oliver heeded warnings to turn off the airconditioning, lest the engine overheat. Foolishly, we tried winding down the windows only to be wrapped in a suffocating blanket of burning air. We learned quickly it was better to sweat inside the airless car and wait until we were over the mountains and on the endlessly long 5 Freeway.

Several hours later, drenched in sweat, we were within reach of our destination. On that road there were things we'd never seen before—thousands of corn fed cows, trucks piled high with oranges, lemons and tomatoes. And on all sides, oil pumps rhythmically lifting and lowering deep into the dry ground. We saw evidence of recent forest fires as well. Miles of blackened hillsides reminded us that wind, combined with intense heat, was a very real threat that time of year to the landscape and livelihood of farmers.

Our appointment the next day was held in a building that resembled a five-star hotel, nestled within a nondescript city park. In the lobby stood a large marble table adorned with oversized fresh floral arrangements, a reception desk with no guests to attend, and a grand piano—the kind that makes you do a double take. The piano stool was empty, yet the music was live, echoing upwards through the vast entrance as each key was pressed down in perfect fingerless synchronicity. Was it Mozart? Bach, perhaps. Either way, Mathilda couldn't grasp how it actually played music until I explained that it was electronically programmed and therefore didn't need a pianist. I took her over to the large window. Nearing the keyboard, her head dropped and tongue rolled. I held her up so she could go on enjoying this novelty whilst appreciating that cataplexy, the transparent giveaway of her emotions, meant I could actually see that sometimes, she was really happy.

The three of us rode the elevator up to the sleep clinic and to another reception desk where we filled out pages upon pages of paperwork before seeing any medical professionals. Oliver and I signed our names, possibly a half a dozen times, not really understanding the details pertaining to litigation or costs that several weeks later would arrive at our apartment. Finally, we sat down, weary and anxious. I felt every last bit of energy drain from me. We had made it. We had arrived at Stanford, the place that had been a symbol of hope and the focus of all our efforts over the last year. We were here on time, the last two days, weeks, and months behind us.

The appointment itself was anything but remarkable. There was the usual triage of measuring weight, blood pressure and temperature followed by a barrage of questions from a junior doctor. With these preliminaries taken care of, we proceeded to meet Dr. Emmanuel Mignot, Professor of Sleep Medicine and Director of the Stanford Center for Sleep Sciences. In his disarming French accent, he did his best to put our weary souls at ease, bringing an air of familiarity and effortless insouciance with his light touch. I should have anticipated the host of other doctors in the small room with him, all waiting to see the youngest person with narcolepsy in the world. Instead, it reinforced the unique challenges of our situation and the potential complexities we faced. As for Mathilda, she treated it like any other appointment, turning her back on the doctors and falling asleep. At one point, Dr. Mignot made it clear that twenty percent of people with narcolepsy do not respond to treatment. Slowly, this figure became larger in our minds than either of us could deal with. Oliver shot me a terrifying look that said, *"20 percent? What if she's in that percentage? We've just arrived here, sold everything and relocated half way round the world—it doesn't bear thinking about!"* For myself, I tried to believe she was in the eighty percent who would do well on Xyrem. Surely, the odds were in her favor?

Later that afternoon after Mathilda's blood was drawn, we met Mali, Dr. Mignot's personal assistant, in her office. She gave Oliver a *Wake up Narcolepsy* t-shirt, one that he still wears to bed and to work under his shirts when it's cooler. We chatted a while and briefly met another family with a fourteen-year-old sufferer. I thought her remarkably upbeat despite her mom claiming she had undergone a massive personality shift for the worse since the onset of narcolepsy. But most important for us all that day, we left Mali's office with a prescription for Xyrem.

Not long after, Mathilda would receive the treatment we'd come for. She began sleeping in blocks of two hours each night for the next several months, followed by mornings of throwing up, headaches and dramatic weight loss. Titrating the right dose for her took the better part of the next year. The dosage increased each week, which controlled many of her symptoms, especially hypnogogic hallucinations and EDS. Then followed appointments with an Ear, Nose and

Throat (ENT) doctor; surgery for sleep apnea at the LA children's hospital; a palate expander to open her airways; and new daytime medications to treat what remained of her cataplexy. She participated in numerous overnight sleep studies, revealing that she also suffered from the sleep disorders central sleep apnea and parasomnia. Sleep disorders, it would seem, often come in clusters.

I stumbled across several online research papers written by leading sleep scientists who cited Mathilda as a British three-year-old child with narcolepsy and cataplexy. These studies linked the onset of her symptoms to the H1N1 Pandemrix Vaccine.

Since Xyrem was beginning to work slowly on her nighttime symptoms and cataplexy, she started kindergarten that fall at a local public school. She took daytime naps, now condensed, on a plinth in the nurse's office before finding her way back to the classroom where she learned to read again, only this time in Spanish.

We found a different school for Liberty and Elliot almost a year later, one that taught exactly the same curriculum we had studied at home. I thought the transition from home life to institutionalized learning would be overwhelming since neither of them had ever stepped inside a school until that day. But St. Monica Academy was small enough to feel like a family and caring enough to understand that they had been impacted profoundly by their sister's condition.

The two of them slipped into their new routines almost effortlessly, playing basketball, making dozens of friends, and becoming active members at our church youth group. In many ways their transition to a new culture and educational system was seamless, save for Liberty's hankering for home and the simplicity of our old routines. Years later, still she would fiercely maintain her British identity, accent and love of England, the people she had left behind. We all did, to some extent, but I could never quite shake off how both the government and the health service ultimately had failed our family. There was an overriding need within me to try to let go of the past and move on.

Having spent a year in the apartment, we found a place we now call home—a Californian ranch house with views across the back yard to the San Gabriel Mountains. When it rains, which is not often, the hills turn a vibrant green overnight and the lawns sparkle, as do the citrus trees and roses that line our street. On especially tired mornings, the year-round color of the native plants—jacarandas, cacti and palm trees—continues to lift our spirits.

In the years since, I have often asked myself if I would ever have chosen this diagnosis. Not that one has a say in these things, but it has crossed my mind nonetheless. And since it is not I that suffers with narcolepsy, the answer will always be a resounding *no. Of course not.* There are few things more unbearable than witnessing your child suffer day and night, knowing she will be shaped by her illness for the rest of their life. It is nearly unendurable to realize that Mathilda will wrestle not only with the symptoms of narcolepsy for the rest of her life, but also the fact that it will impact all her relationships, her occupational options and her own family life, should she ever live independently.

But it's complicated. In large part, we love living here and remain deeply grateful for the opportunity for treatment despite all the headaches and expenses that come with it. Rarely a week goes by without having to speak to pharmacists and our insurance company to ensure the delivery of her medication. Yet, seeing Mathilda able to leave the house without needing to be carried, laughing without falling   down, and sleeping for a few hours without hallucinating, is like a miracle. One that has come with a price, and not just financial.

Sitting here now, at a little green table in our front yard, under a canopy of ancient oaks that filter fingers of light between their strong limbs, I see the children's flip flops strewn across the front door mat. Gone are the little red Wellington boots and child-sized umbrellas. Several adult sized swimsuits and towels are draped over the chair and are drying rapidly in the heat. And in an hour or so

I will drive on the freeway to pick up the children from school. On the way home, Elliot will talk non-stop of his day, the unfairness of homework, and the friends he wants over on Friday. Liberty will be asking what's planned for the weekend so she can plan her social life around her Saturday job as a life-guard. Mathilda will sleep, wake up fractious and unreachable as we pull into the driveway, and require help changing out of her uniform. Then, for the next five hours, we will see a glimmer of the girl we once knew. She will sing in her room, feed the cats, and complain when the dog messes up her game. Over supper she will talk incessantly and need encouragement to eat. Finally, she will refuse to shower and move toward her bedroom before beginning another night of waking, medication, sleeping, and eating.

There is little I can say that is good about the condition, or caring for a child who does not remember what it's like to sleep soundly. Narcolepsy is an invisible form of torture in its own way, one that steals time, and threatens to suck all pleasure out of life. But I can say that good has come from it. Like many people world-wide, I understand that each 24-hour period is fraught with the kind of challenges that give one an entirely different perspective. I have learned that, although the pace is very fast here, life has slowed down in many ways. Each moment of happiness is more delightful, and each accomplishment deserves celebration. And as the sun bows in a blazing farewell each evening to the west of the City of Angels, I remain grateful for feeling more deeply, loving more tenderly, and realizing that our little family is all the stronger for enduring these past years together.

I've seen the best and worst in people, realized the best and worst in myself, and become filled with a new purpose. Caring for a loved one is not glamorous, or easy. I'm not paid for it, nor is what I do each day and night objectively measurable. My role as a caregiver, a vocation that is shared with thousands of other parents, will never hit the headlines, impact research data or change the world. But I believe it will do this: for that one child that is entrusted to me with her uncommon ailments and symptoms, I have the unique burden of raising Mathilda with the same potential that is available to every human being. She may be beset by the symptoms and the limitations that come with narcolepsy, yet with the right counsel, and consistent care, Mathilda can realistically hope for a future that is bright, indeed. What greater purpose could I have as a parent than to lead my chronically sick child toward the life intended for her, one that is filled with potential and promise? Recognizing the realities my daughter faces and at the same time equipping her to be anything she wants to be might be one of the most meaningful tasks of my life.

At the end of each night shift with Mathilda, however, still I crawl toward the coffee pot wondering if the fog will rise high enough for me to do all that is required of me. And yet, even on a few broken hours of sleep and, six years in, somehow each morning I find the energy to do what needs to be done, with the same smile, I hope, and a sweeter spirit. During this time I have travelled to the very outskirts of what I thought possible of enduring physically, and emotionally. Some days I have been stuck there on my knees with grief. On others, I have escaped, filled with the limitless beauty of those around me and the hope stored within the newness of each day.

In writing our journey, I hope in some small way to illuminate the myths surrounding narcolepsy and to have testified to the resolve and courage of a young girl who does not remember life before the H1N1 vaccine. It is a story that we share with the fifteen hundred children in Europe that similarly developed narcolepsy in 2010. In all, it is estimated there are three million people with narcolepsy worldwide, and many more who remain undiagnosed. Through my blog and through social media, I have learned that many are on the same journey, fighting for treatment they hope will relieve some of their symptoms. A few lose this battle. Unable to envision a future worth living, they take their lives and leave their families broken with grief.

During the last few months of our time in England, I received a card from my friends Julie and Matt Canliss. On the front was a familiar quote by the English thirteenth-century mystic, Julian of Norwich: *All shall be well, all* shall be well, all manner of things shall be well. The card's message of hope resounded within, but I found something my friends had written particularly meaningful at the time. They went on to cite Jerome: *"Pity those who are not under persecution, for they have no reason to be awake."* Then, they closed in their own words: *"so that in many ways when we are with you we are but dwarves amongst giants."* Julie and Matt felt a certain privilege in sharing our journey in Mathilda's suffering. They knew as parents of four children what fatigue felt like. But they also recognized that our task in raising Mathilda was a whole new level of exhaustion.

Since moving here, I've had the privilege of meeting adults and children with narcolepsy, and those words have come back to me on occasion. I, in turn, have felt like a dwarf amongst giants in the presence of their determination to lead a near-normal life despite its challenges. Their example has given me hope for Mathilda, for her future and ours. When I see her wake up each day able to draw, to play, and to attend birthday parties, there's not a moment that goes by when I regret the choices we made to bring her here.

When I asked Oliver to consider giving up his job and to find another, one that would secure specialist care and treatment for Mathilda, it was plea I made only once. His burden at the time, loaded and fraught with professional and personal responsibility, was tempered by a wrought-iron determination to do the best he could, given the limitations we were working with. I believe that his resolution, coupled with the philosophy I had been raised with—to never ever give up—provided us with a vision that held our family together. We are blest that, to this day, Oliver still teaches, writes academic books on philosophical theology, and travels to give lectures all over the world. He has remained a full-time loving, caring and wonderful father to our growing children. I've since found that side of him both humbling and inspiring. He achieved something I couldn't have at the time, something that has cost him and that not many others would have found the resolve to do.

This love of ours, however vulnerable, has been enough to carry me through the darkest nights of our daughter's brain dysfunction, through the peculiar imbalance a sick child throws at a family, and through our journey across the Atlantic to America. Then, without any remorse, all five of us came up for air—up and out on the other side of adversity.

From time to time, I pull out that card that lies beneath a pile of paperwork in a kitchen drawer—as if being here I need reminding: *All shall be well, all shall be well, all manner of things shall be well.*

Acknowledgements

It's been said that it takes a whole village to raise a child. Something similar is required when writing a book. I'd like to thank the following people for their encouragement in the early draft of this manuscript: Timothy Gombis, Nada Jones, Tabitha and Kelly Kapic, Adrianna Petryna, Jen Rosner, Eleonore Stump and Darrel Walters.

And those at the Pasadena Writers Salon, Kim Khoehler, Elizabeth Hughes, Mary Keller, Jonathan Rothell and Lauren Marlis. Your positive insight and gentle criticism kept me writing on the many occasions when I felt like throwing the towel in.

Special thanks are due to all those who supported us in Bristol when things became rough, including Joanna Bacon, Jan Bartlett, Julie and Matt Canlis, Mary Ferguson, Penny Fernandez, Jan Haime, Sam Kemp, Rod Symmons and Peter and Christina Wood. I am particularly thankful to Wendy Evans who patiently stepped in with schooling Liberty and Elliot when Mathilda was in the hospital. She was my shoulder to lean and cry on when I returned home. Your presence in my life is still something I miss.

Similarly, I am indebted to everyone in Princeton who

helped look after the children when we first flew out here to interview and for our wonderful year before it all started. Thank you Corrie and Shane Berg, Joao and Adrianna Biehl, Mimi and John Bowlin and Gail and Luke Powery.

And where we would be without the support of the faculty at Fuller? From the bottom of my heart, thank you Howard Loewen and Rich Mouw for making our move possible. Thank you John and Marianne Thompson and Mark and Janette Labberton for your ongoing kindness and support.

Our parents have loved us every step of the way and graciously accepted the decision we made in finding treatment for Mathilda by relocating half way across the globe. They have sacrificed watching their grandchildren grow up, and we have lost much of their positive influence on their lives. John and Jean Wright and Chris and Julia Crisp—we are ever grateful for you.

And to my beautiful sister Amanda, who has been a constant source of support and joy, despite being thousands of miles away. Thank you, sweet girl, for partnering with me in raising a child with special needs. I'll always see you through my love goggles. To my brother-in-law James and nephew Lucas who always make their trips over here the best of fun. Thank you for those precious memories.

And to my uncle Fred Wylds for turning up on our Pasadena doorstep every few months with his huge sense of British charisma. Who'd have thought we'd follow you from

London to the sunny shores of SoCal?

Peter Todd—thank you for your legal advice and encouragement to just tell the story as it happened and for being willing to fight for treatment and justice for the British families affected by the 2010 H1N1 vaccine.

For friends here in Los Angeles who scooped us up after landing, accepted us for all our limitations and cultural differences and taught us how to laugh again. Thank you Laura and Jason Berns, Virginia Christman and Alan Brown, Cynthia and Nord Eriksson, Erin Dufault-Hunter, Bridget Lacerte, Tommy and Kim Givens, Jenny and Jeremy Green, Kendall Migliozzi, Tanya Pitre, Pam and Scott Wessling, and Wendy and Rich Yee.

Marcus and Joy Stenzel, thank you for being sensitive, accommodating and generous. Your tenderness helped us emerge from the shadows.

Special thanks to James and Rebecca Farlow for their unlimited patience and tech support with my blog and in the final stages of publication of this manuscript. "Coming Soon" has become "Now Available." Thank you dear friends.

Darian and Nicole Lockett and Matt Jenson have been a family to us over the past six years. For friendship, pool parties, car loans and cousins—a heartfelt thanks. It is difficult to imagine how our relocation would have turned out without your unrelenting commitment to us all. I am deeply grateful.

To the staff at Saint Monica Academy that accepted three disoriented British children several years ago. For their faithful education and care of them five days a week, especially Vanessa Anderson, Alexandra Currie, Jane Forsyth, Marguerite Grimm, Peter Halpin, Hugh O'Donnell, Jessica Guiterrez, Judy Guiterrez, Jack Goodwin, Mary Putman, Marisela Miranda, Therese Naaden, Colleen Smith and Erin Talbot. Few schools can deliver academic rigor and spiritual support for a family such as ours. Thank you for accommodating Mathilda as she naps in the classroom, cries during recess and is late on homework. Not only that; thank you also for recognizing the unique path of Libby and Elliot and supporting them as individuals.

Thanks to our supportive community of friends at Knox Presbyterian in Pasadena, especially Matt Colwell, Davin and Heather Thomsen Tang, and Rebecca Turner who faithfully mentor our children. A heartfelt thank you to Brian and Ally Lee who provided us with faithful friendship and weekends of respite care.

Special thanks to Calise Green, my very own Nigella Lawson, for many meals and faithful friendship. Your capacity to love unconditionally is an incredible blessing and example. Thank you, Jonathon Green, for your exceptional cover art. You both are talented in a myriad of ways, and I remain deeply grateful for your presence in our lives.

I will always be indebted immensely to the team at Stanford Center for Narcolepsy Research, for their world-class care, gentle bedside manner and prompt replies to desperate emails and phone calls. Thank you Mali Einen, an incredible lifeline and advocate for Children with narcolepsy who began her rescue back in England and who has since become a friend. I cannot imagine how our lives would have played out had you not been instrumental in Mathilda's road to restoration. A huge bow is due to Dr. Emmanuel Mignot, for being a light to children that suffer with narcolepsy, not in the least of whom was our then three, now ten-year-old. Thank you. Thank you.

I remain deeply grateful for friends in the wider narcolepsy community—they have shown me hope, inspiration and friendship: Jayne Collins, Julie Flygare, Monica Gow, Julea Steiner, Lindsay Jesteadt, Heather Wray-Fogg, Andee Coppel and many others.

Special thanks to Wake Up Narcolepsy for providing me with an opportunity to help other families who live with the challenges of narcolepsy and giving tangible hope through funding research.

Mathilda still might not be diagnosed if it were not for the brilliant Dr. Siddarth Shah, who swept into our lives for just two days back in May of 2010. His brief encounter with us changed the trajectory of our lives forever. I don't really know how to thank you enough for your role, descending and then disappearing like an angel. You listened with intent, withheld judgment and ignored your colleagues. Thank you for being clinically confident enough to look into the mind of a three-year-old who was suffering but could not find the words to tell you.

To all the readers of my blog, claireccrisp.com: thank you for your comments, feedback and dialogue. Thank you especially for supporting my work over the last year and being willing to engage in conversation over the important issues pertaining to narcolepsy and parenting our children afflicted with the condition. I've learnt so much from you all.

To Marisela Miranda, my brilliant editor who patiently cleaned the manuscript and improved every page. Thanks aren't enough.

Thank you Linda Huang for reading through the second draft and making helpful comments from beginning to end.

This story wouldn't exist without the incredible talent and sacrifice of my beloved Oliver. I'm not sure if I'll ever be able to communicate the depth of my gratitude for you— my editor, friend, supervisor, husband, early morning annoying brother, cheerleader, sounding board, encourager, and advisor. A million thanks for your tenacity, gentleness, honest feedback and trust in me to tell our story. You've been beyond generous in enabling this dream to come true. If this book ever makes a dime, dinner's on me. Here's to moving forward together and realizing our dreams of growing old side by side.

A lifetime of heartfelt thanks go to our older two children, Liberty Alice and Elliot Anselm. Thank you for going the extra mile with chores at home, respecting that Mum was writing and running late on pick-up. I truly appreciate your gracious acceptance of our new life in a new place, the energy with which you face each day, and the way you accommodate Mathilda's needs and ours. You are an inspiration, a ray of sunlight and the very best company there is. Over the past six years, I have often lamented the daily impact that narcolepsy has had on you both, and what it has taken from your own childhoods. And yet, I have witnessed an incredible tendency toward empathy and kindness within you and a remarkable bond that you share as partners. I am ever grateful for your mature intuition, humor and hard work. Thank you for graciously bearing the responsibilities that have been yours uniquely.

Mathilda Anais: I have the utmost respect for how you have faced your fear of hospitals and doctors, for how you tackle each day and night, and for how you are growing into a young woman with narcolepsy. Our many hours of caring for you have provided an uncommon bond despite the fears and frustrations that come with the condition. Thank you for showing me the furthest outposts of wakefulness, the depths of sleepy despair and the giddying heights of hope. Brave, bold and beautiful—this journey is yours, one that you've shared with us and many other children with narcolepsy. Know that in the weariness of every day and the lonely, lingering dark hours each night as you search for sleep, you are, indeed, mighty in battle. And you, my little lady, are not alone.

A Note From Claire

Thank you of reading Waking Mathilda—A Memoir of Childhood Narcolepsy.

If you loved the book I would really appreciate a review on Amazon. Your views matter to me and help others decide if they too should read it. Also, feel free to pass on the book to someone who you think might benefit from our story.

Want to connect with me? I'd love to hear from you. Here's where I hang out (online) when not stuck in LA traffic or dancing at Zumba.

Website/blog: www.claireccrisp.com
Facebook: /clairecrisp
Instagram: londonerinla
Twitter:@ClaireCrisp1

Thanks in advance,

Claire

CLAIRE CRISP

Born and raised in London, Claire Crisp worked as physical therapist in the British National Health Service as well as in private practice. She went on to teach her three children at home for the next decade in Scotland, the US and England. From 2010 onwards Claire has been a full-time caregiver to her daughter Mathilda who developed narcolepsy as a result of the H1N1 vaccine. The family movd from their home in England to California, securing treatment for Mathilda at the Stanford Center for Narcolepsy Research. She is an award-winning advocate for children with narcolepsy, a speaker and blogger.

Her story has been featured in the Daily Mail, The Independent online, and on Only Human, a WNYC podcast.